D1458752

Commu involvement in health development

An examination of the critical issues

Peter Oakley
University of Reading
England

DISPOSED OF
BY LIBRARY
HOUSE OF LORDS

World Health Organization
Geneva, 1989

ISBN 92 4 156126 2

© World Health Organization, 1989

Publications of the World Health Organization enjoy copyright protection in accordance with the provisions of Protocol 2 of the Universal Copyright Convention. For rights of reproduction or translation of WHO publications, in part or *in toto*, application should be made to the Office of Publications, World Health Organization, Geneva, Switzerland. The World Health Organization welcomes such applications.

The designations employed and the presentation of the material in this publication do not imply the expression of any opinion whatsoever on the part of the Secretariat of the World Health Organization concerning the legal status of any country, territory, city or area or of its authorities, or concerning the delimitation of its frontiers or boundaries.

The mention of specific companies or of certain manufacturers' products does not imply that they are endorsed or recommended by the World Health Organization in preference to others of a similar nature that are not mentioned. Errors and omissions excepted, the names of proprietary products are distinguished by initial capital letters.

The author alone is responsible for the views expressed in this publication.

TYPESET IN INDIA
PRINTED IN ENGLAND

88/7680—Macmillan/Clays—6500

Contents

Foreword

In the past decade, enormous efforts, both intellectual and practical, have been made to devise strategies to improve the lives of the many millions of disadvantaged people in the world. In these efforts, an important concept is the central importance of the people themselves participating in the decisions, and in the implementation and management of development programmes and projects. Participation has been widely recognized as both a basic right of people and of central importance to the success of development efforts.

Naturally, therefore, the link has been made between participation and programmes designed to improve people's health. Many people in the world do not have ready access to health services, and must rely on local knowledge and traditional practices for health care. There is, therefore, a fund of local experience and resources in many parts of the world which could be mobilized to support health programmes. Most countries have at least the elements of a national health structure and in many cases its effectiveness would be increased if local people could contribute to and play a part in its functioning. Community involvement in health development (CIH) has emerged as an imaginative new approach which seeks to bring together the formal, professional health structure and local people with their knowledge and resources.

WHO has played an important role in the promotion of CIH. Since the late 1970s it has actively supported a range of activities which have begun to examine CIH in different fields of health practice to try to define a clearer strategy. Studies have been conducted in over twenty countries and work is continuing in thirteen others. CIH is central to WHO's strategy for health for all, and needs to be considered by all health professionals and administrators in devising programmes for health promotion.

The basic purpose of this book is to bring together the wide-ranging thinking on and interpretations of CIH. It is an attempt to distil an increasing amount of material and present in a clear and concise form the essential elements of CIH. It is intended to serve as a guide for the health professionals who support the idea of CIH and seek to put it into practice, but do not have the time to review a vast amount of material.

This publication is a milestone in the work of WHO on CIH, signifying the move from talk to action that is taking place in many countries. But action is being hindered by lack of skills, by structural and organizational obstacles, and by lack of tried and tested methods for setting criteria and measuring progress in CIH. WHO is intensifying its efforts in these areas in particular through focusing on district health systems based on primary health care, where national health policies and strategies can be harmonized with local needs, initiatives and resources, resulting in participatory development and better health for all people.

Dr H.M. Kahssay
Division of Strengthening of Health Services
World Health Organization
Geneva, Switzerland

Preface

The notion of community involvement in health care has a long tradition, but it is only in the past ten years or so that community involvement in health development (CIH) has emerged as a systematic approach to the subject. CIH is widely acknowledged to be essential to the development of health services, particularly in developing countries, where the process of involving the community in other aspects of development, such as agriculture, has already begun. A number of publications are now available which seek to explain the concept of CIH and it has begun to influence the health sector through, for example, primary health care (PHC), tropical disease control and clean water supply. The proceedings of seminars, workshops and meetings held to discuss and analyse CIH have added to the volume of published material.

In June 1985, a WHO inter-regional meeting on CIH was held on the island of Brioni in Yugoslavia, which in addition to reviewing regional and country experience singled out a number of issues critical to the understanding and practice of CIH. The present review is based on the report of the Brioni meeting and seeks essentially to deal in more depth with the issues discussed in it, particularly by analysing the pertinent literature and expanding the conclusions drawn. It is thus an attempt to explain the reasoning underlying the report of the inter-regional meeting and to develop the arguments set forth therein.[a] The facts that most of the literature on CIH has been published in the last ten years and that the concept has been applied in a very wide range of contexts have underlined the need for a single text discussing CIH theory and practice and the main issues involved. This publication seeks to meet that need. It makes no claims to be a definitive text on the subject.

---

[a] *Community involvement for health development: report of the inter-regional meeting, Brioni, Yugoslavia, 9–14 June 1985.* Unpublished WHO document, SHS/85.8.

At present, knowledge of how CIH is applied in practice is quite limited since in general its implementation has not been on a wide scale and has not therefore been described in widely accessible sources. This book does contain, however, a number of direct references to CIH practice in the belief that a more systematic understanding of that practice will promote wider adoption of CIH as an approach to health development.

Another purpose of this book is to serve as an introduction and source of information for health professionals who are already, or expect to become, involved in CIH as a health strategy. By considering material drawn from a wide range of texts, it pinpoints the critical issues that health professionals will have to consider in implementing CIH. It is neither a training manual nor a detailed review of national policy options. It should, however, be of use to health professionals and to the staff and students of health and training institutions who have to determine how the CIH concept can best be translated into practical measures. As more information accumulates the essential aspects of CIH will need to be studied in greater detail. The book should, therefore, be seen as an initial step towards clarifying conceptual and practical issues in order to broaden understanding of the potential of CIH as an effective health strategy.

The first two chapters examine community participation and community involvement in health development and describe the variety of interpretations that have been given to the two concepts. The longest chapter is Chapter 3, which examines a number of the essential issues involved. Each of these is considered in some detail and suggestions are made on how best to deal with them. The final chapter sums up the current position with regard to CIH and suggests a number of steps that could be taken to use it more effectively as a strategy for health development.

The author acknowledges with thanks the comments made on an earlier draft of this review by Ian Askew, Jan Branckaerts, Marie-Therese Feuerstein, Stephen Frankel, John Hastings, Barbara Israel, Reijo Salmela, Susan Rifkin, Alistair White and Helmut Wintersberger. Those comments, both individually and collectively, were most useful in producing the final version.

Chapter 1

The basis of CIH

Introduction

Any discussion of the concept and practice of CIH must begin by examining what is commonly called the 'development process'. Health development is an important element in the development process in general and is therefore influenced in practice by different perceptions of what constitutes development and what causes underdevelopment. Until the early 1970s the development process was largely dominated by attempts on the part of development planners and workers to modernize and improve the technical performance of the physical assets of a particular country or area. In the health field this approach led to an emphasis on building up the health infrastructure at different levels and introducing health practices based on 'western' concepts of health care. Since the early 1970s, however, a fundamental reappraisal of the nature and content of the development process has been under way and has inevitably influenced thinking on health practice and development (*1, 2*).

The essential feature of this reappraisal has been the concept of 'participation', i.e. the idea that, whatever material form the development process may take, the active participation of the people in any activities proposed or undertaken must be encouraged. This concept has given rise to a flood of publications and the idea of participation is now part and parcel of most forms of developmental activity. This is not the place, however, to examine this vast corpus of literature on participation, except to say that two main schools of thought seem to have emerged:

(i) One school makes the assumption that there is little generally wrong with the direction of the development process and that past failures have largely occurred because the human element has been neglected and people have not wanted to involve themselves in projects about which they had little information or of whose value they were not convinced. This assumption

1

has been the basis of measures to fill the gap, to provide more information and to increase the knowledge of the local people concerned. It is believed that this information and knowledge will persuade people to become involved, to commit themselves, and thus help ensure the success of the project or programme.

(ii) The other school argues that the direction of the development process is fundamentally misconceived. It is not the failure to take the human factor into account that is at fault, but rather the unreflecting way in which people have been left out of the development equation and treated as passive recipients rather than active participants. The new approach, therefore, is to seek innovative and flexible procedures, taking into account the knowledge already possessed by local people. Participation in this sense is concerned with the production of knowledge, new directions and new modes of organization, rather than with the wider dissemination of the procedures adopted hitherto.

Clearly these two interpretations of participation are very different; it could indeed be argued that they are diametrically opposed to each other. What matters is to recognize that they exist and may result in equally different forms of practice. There is no single universally valid interpretation of participation. It must be stated, however, that the analysis of the content, trends and practice of CIH in this study is based on the second of the two concepts outlined above.

Whatever the underlying assumptions, however, all ideas of participation agree that people must be given a voice in development decisions, access to the resources and knowledge required for development and a share in the benefits achieved. Participation in development is a multidimensional process which varies from area to area, depending on local circumstances. There are many ways of looking at it and its interpretation very much depends on the approach to development adopted (3).

Participation and health

In view of what has been outlined above, there has been an increasing tendency to give favourable consideration to the notion of local participation in health policy and services. There is overwhelming evidence that the majority of the world's people have no regular access to organized health services. Most people in the world in fact confront the diseases and illnesses that plague them with little, if any, formal support and under conditions of scarce food and financial resources. In most developing countries the formal health services are able to provide coverage for only a small proportion of the people they are supposed to look after (4). In coping with the problems of how to stay alive and healthy, millions of poor people have little to support them but their own knowledge and efforts (5).

In response to this situation, the aim of achieving health for all by the year 2000 has been adopted as a basic tenet of health policy and development. In the first instance it could be argued that its achievement depends largely on the eradication of poverty and that the actions required are therefore largely outside the realm of medicine and public health proper. Health for all, therefore, is not exclusively an issue of health policy and development. The obstacles in the way of achieving it are daunting. These obstacles are not primarily due to a lack of medical knowledge; indeed it might be argued that, given the appropriate mechanisms and support, the scientific knowledge needed to radically improve the health of the majority of the world's population already exists and that what is mainly required is knowledge of how to achieve the massive, widespread involvement of people themselves, not just in supporting the health services and enabling them to function, but what is more important, in determining health priorities and how to allocate scarce health resources. Community participation has therefore, come to be seen as a way of rapidly improving the health services available for the majority of the world's people. Indeed it is argued that even if the structural changes required are carried out, health for all will be unachievable by the year 2000 unless radically different forms of health care are instituted that tap local manpower and resources and are essentially people's services and not services designed and maintained by external government health representatives. This argument, however, must be considered in relation to the current distribution of health resources within a particular country and should not be interpreted as throwing the onus of providing the resources for health care entirely upon local communities (6,7).

The arguments for CIH

Inevitably, fresh thinking on development practices has led in the different sectors to critical reviews of previous practices and arguments in favour of change. In the past eight years or so the emergence of the CIH concept has led to widespread reconsideration of previous practices, determination of where they went wrong

3

and proposals for the changes that are needed. The formal concept of CIH seems to date from the mid-1970s and since then a wide range of publications have argued its merits and suggested the kinds of change it would bring about. It would appear from the literature that CIH has been enthusiastically welcomed as the fundamental change in direction required to promote effective health development.

Advantages of a community participation approach

(i)   A community participation approach is a cost-effective way of extending a health care system to the geographical and social periphery of a country – although it is far from cost-free.

(ii)   Communities that begin to understand their health status objectively rather than fatalistically may be moved to take a series of preventive measures.

(iii)   Communities that invest labour, time, money and materials in health-promoting activities are more committed to the use and maintenance of the things they produce, such as water supplies.

(iv)   Health education is most effective as part and parcel of village activities.

(v)   Community health workers, if they are well chosen, have the people's confidence. They may know the most effective techniques for achieving commitment from their neighbours and, at the very least, are not likely to exploit them. They come under strong social pressure to help the community carry out its health-promoting activities. However, they must also have dependable supplies and support from the higher levels of the health service.

MacCormack, C. P. Community participation in primary health care. *Tropical doctor*, **13** (2): 51–54 (1983)

The arguments in favour of CIH are not only convincing but also fairly uniform throughout the literature and are frequently based on an analysis of past errors. Health development is not a recent phenomenon but, like the development of other sectors such as agriculture, has long been an important aspect of both national and regional development plans. Criticisms of previous health development strategies, particularly those linked to the notion of community involvement, suggest four main reasons for their lack of success (*8*):

(i)   They failed to encourage people to think or act for themselves in attempting to solve their health problems, impelling them to rely upon external sources for action and solutions.

(ii) Failure to provide adequate training led to local people being unable to maintain the services that had been set up. Those services could not, therefore, be sustained by local resources and knowledge.

(iii) In the past there have been cases of communities contributing resources and manpower to health projects and programmes, but there has been little active community involvement in their design and implementation.

(iv) The conflict between health-directed needs, as determined by the health service and medical profession, and health-related needs, such as housing, water and sanitation, as determined by local people themselves. This conflict often results in an incompatibility between the two sets of needs and a lack of community interest in externally promoted health programmes.

CIH has, therefore, emerged as the antidote to the deficiencies outlined above and the arguments in favour of it have been extensively discussed in the literature. Each of the rather similar reasons for failure listed above underlines the critical importance of local involvement if health programmes and projects are to succeed. Several studies set forth arguments for adopting CIH as a strategy for health development and the following is a composite list of those arguments taken from several sources (*8–10*):

(i)   CIH is a basic right, which all people should be able to enjoy. Involvement in the decisions and actions that affect people's health builds self-esteem and also encourages a sense of responsibility. CIH as a principle is of intrinsic value in the development of communities in a wider sense and should be promoted as the basic approach to health development.

(ii) Many health services, particularly in developing countries, function on the basis of limited resources. CIH can be a means of making more resources available by drawing upon local knowledge and resources to complement what is provided by the formal health services. Furthermore, it can help to extend the coverage of health services and to lower their overall cost.

5

CIH can also make health services more cost-effective and lead in the long term to an adequate return on funds invested in the health sector. It is not, however, a substitute for formal health services or a mechanism of double taxation.

(iii) CIH increases the possibility that health programmes and projects will be appropriate and successful in meeting health needs as defined by local people, as opposed to medical needs as defined by the health authorities. When health services take into account local perceptions of health needs and are managed with the support of local people, there will be a better chance of their programmes being successful.

(iv) CIH breaks the knot of dependence that characterizes much health development work and, on a wider front, makes local people aware that they could become usefully involved in development in general. Ultimately CIH can help to make people politically conscious and eager to make their voice heard in regard to development processes in their country or area.

Comment

In theory at least, health professionals seem to support CIH as a basic principle to be followed in health development. CIH has become a widely accepted concept and doubts about its need or appropriateness are rarely formally expressed. The literature reflects this commitment to CIH, which it supports with persuasive arguments. Among the guiding principles agreed at Alma-Ata and embodied in the health-for-all strategy, for example, is the participation of people in health development. If judgements were based solely on the professional literature it might well be concluded that CIH as a strategy for health development was now firmly entrenched in the minds of those who are responsible for formulating health policy and managing its implementation.

It has to be acknowledged, however, that because of its relative newness as a strategy of health development, the theory of CIH is probably somewhat ahead of its practice. Although there are an increasing number of examples of CIH being applied in a variety of different contexts, as a fundamental principle of formal health service practice it is still largely underdeveloped. It was in view of this that a WHO inter-regional meeting on CIH was held in Brioni in Yugoslavia in June 1985 to examine various aspects of CIH practice. That meeting singled out a number of problems that needed further consideration, and which form the basis of this book.

References and notes

1. Haque, W. et al. Towards a theory of rural development. *Development dialogue*, No. 2: 7–137 (1977).

2. Galjart, B. Counterdevelopment: a position paper. *Community development journal*, **16**: 88–96 (1981).

3. The literature on the concept and practice of participation in different fields of development has grown enormously in recent years. A few examples include: Uphoff, N. T. & Cohen, J. *Feasibility and application of rural development participation: a state-of-the-art paper*, Ithaca, NY, Cornell University, 1979; Oakley, P. & Marsden, D. *Approaches to participation in rural development*, Geneva, International Labour Office, 1985; and Galjart, B. & Buijs, D., ed. *Participation of the poor in development*, Leiden, University of Leiden, 1982.

4. Extension of health service coverage using primary care and community participation strategies. *Bulletin of the Pan American Health Organization*, **XI**: 345–369 (1977).

5. Newell, K. W. Helping people help themselves. *World health*, April 1975, pp. 3–7.

6. Rifkin, S. Community participation: a planner's approach. *Contact*, Special series No. 3: 1–8 (1980).

7. Donoso, G. Health care and community action. *WHO Chronicle*, **32**: 102–105 (1978).

8. Fonaroff, A. *Community involvement in health systems for primary health care.* Unpublished WHO document SHS/83.6.

9. *Community participation and tropical disease control – an exercise in participatory research.* Unpublished WHO document, TDR/SER/SWG, 1983.

10. *Global Strategy for Health For All by the Year 2000.* Geneva, World Health Organization, 1981 ("Health for All" Series, No. 3).

Chapter 2

Understanding CIH

Introduction

The concept of CIH emerged as a result of concern to encourage local participation in all aspects of development, including health development. CIH means local participation in the design and delivery of health care services, which is needed for the reasons examined in Chapter 1. Health literature, however, seems in doubt as to whether to use the term 'community involvement' or 'community participation'. In most areas of development preference seems to be given to the term 'community participation' but the health sector seems to have opted for 'community involvement' because of its deeper implications. In primary health care the distinction between the two terms can be seen from the following statement (*1*):

> To be successful [primary health care] needs individual and community self-reliance and the maximum community involvement or participation, that is to say, the active involvement of people living together in some form of social organization and cohesion in the planning, operation and control of primary health care using local, national and other resources. The term 'involvement' is preferable to 'participation' because it implies a deeper and more personal identification of members of the community with primary health care.

Such has been the impact in the past few years of the concept of participation in health development that it has begun to influence thinking in a whole range of related health fields. Since the late 1970s there has been a flood of literature analysing the concept of involvement in various aspects of health development. In the great majority of cases the literature acknowledges the importance of such involvement but, as was to be expected, there is a wide range of interpretations and it is frequently necessary first and foremost to define the terms used. Because it is a fundamental principle of design and implementation, community involvement in health development is open to a variety of interpretations.

Community participation

The concept of CIH cannot be divorced from the broader aim of encouraging the active participation of local people in the development process as a whole. Any understanding of CIH must therefore begin by attempting to understand the concept of participation. And that is where the problem begins. There is no single working interpretation of the concept of participation that has been universally accepted in development work. Indeed there are a variety of different interpretations, each giving rise to a different form of practice. It is important to be aware of this variety of interpretations, since each, in its own way, has profound implications for development practice.

Although there would appear to be widespread agreement on the importance of community participation for bringing about the desired redistribution of the benefits of development, there is less of a consensus on the nature and content of the participation process. A wide range of equivocal terms such as 'self-help', 'self-reliance', 'cooperation' and 'local autonomy' add to the confusion. The following are, for example, three interpretations of participation which reflect quite different concepts of development:

(i) 'Participation means . . . in its broadest sense to sensitize people and thus to increase the receptivity and ability of people to respond to development programmes, as well as to encourage local initiatives' (2).

(ii) 'With regard to development . . . participation includes people's involvement in decision-making processes, in implementing programmes . . . their sharing in the benefits of development programmes and their involvement in efforts to evaluate such programmes' (3).

(iii) 'Participation involves . . . organized efforts to increase control over resources and regulative institutions in given social situations on the part of groups or movements of those hitherto excluded from such control' (4).

These statements bear witness to widely divergent views on the nature of participation in rural development. It is important, however, to reduce these different views to some sort of order if participation is to be subjected to rational analysis. This can be done by

9

distinguishing two broad but very different categories of interpretations of 'participation' which may be regarded as the two ends of a continuum: participation as a means and participation as an end.

Participation as a means

In this interpretation participation is seen as the means of achieving a set objective or goal. In other words it is a way of using the economic and social resources of rural people to achieve pre-determined targets. The *results* of the participation in the shape of the predetermined targets are more important than the *act* of participation. Those results may indeed lead to a welcome improvement in the physical environment of rural people and may well coincide with local needs as perceived by those people.

Government and development agencies responsible for providing services and with the power to control resources see participation as a means of improving the efficiency of their service-delivery systems. This emphasis on improving efficiency categorizes participation as a management technique intended to benefit both provider and consumer. The consumers are coopted into the delivery system and become subject to its dictates. Essentially this is an indirect form of participation. Technically it could be argued that it is representative, since the consumer apparently has some influence on the delivery system, but participation is limited to comment and advice and does not lead to any direct control. Generally speaking sharing in the benefits of the delivery system is the more characteristic outcome of this form of participation.

Participation as a means is essentially a static, passive and ultimately controllable form of participation. It is the form of participation more commonly found in rural development programmes and projects. It is seen there, however, as a temporary feature, an input required if objectives are to be achieved. It is only rarely that a longer-term view is taken. Inevitably the emphasis is on rapid mobilization, direct involvement in the task on hand and the abandonment of participation once the task has been completed. It is rightly argued that rural development projects would benefit from more direct participation by the local people, but it is also important to ensure that such participation is not merely a way of facilitating attainment of the project's objectives.

Participation as an end

Participation in rural development may on the other hand be regarded as an end in itself. Emphasis is then laid on participation as a process in which confidence and solidarity among rural people are built up. In a rural development project, participation as a process is a dynamic, unquantifiable and essentially unpredictable element. It is created and moulded by the participants. It is an active form of participation, responding to local needs and changing circumstances.

The process of participation is seen as a permanent and intrinsic feature of rural development that enhances and strengthens any rural development project. It will not only last the life of the project but, more important, will extend beyond the project's end in the shape of a permanent dynamic involvement. It is not seen merely as a management technique, but rather as a means of enabling rural people to become more directly involved in rural development. The critical elements in the process are to enhance awareness and build up organization, as the two fundamental conditions for effective participation.

More generally, participation as an end in itself presupposes the building-up of influence or involvement from the bottom upwards. As a result this form of participation has come to be associated with development activities outside the formal or government sector and is concerned with building up pressures from below in order to bring about change in existing institutional arrangements. It does not necessarily begin with any preconceived set of quantifiable targets or objectives: it is more concerned with developing a genuine dynamic of analysis and involvement and then allowing the process to follow its natural course.

More detailed analysis of participation as a process shows that there are a number of discrete stages; any participation process can be characterized in terms of the stage it has reached. In the first instance a stage of *marginal participation* can be distinguished, in which participation by the people is limited and transitory and has little direct influence on the outcome of the development activity. In many rural development projects where plans and objectives are determined beforehand, rural people achieve only a marginal influence on performance. At a different level there is a stage of *substantive participation*. At this stage rural people are actively involved in determining priorities and carrying out activities, even if the mechanism for these activities is externally controlled. Substantive participation is the means by which many rural development projects achieve their objectives, but there is evidence that the substance of the participation is limited to the benefits of the project activities. Finally an ultimate stage of *structural participation* may be distinguished. In this case participation is an integral component of the project and the ideological basis for all project activities. In

11

structural participation rural people play an active and direct part in the development process and have the power to ensure that their opinions are heeded.

The richness of the participation concept is reflected in the wide variety of approaches that can be used in its analysis. Thus, some forms of participation can be considered from the standpoint of how they were initiated. In this respect a distinction can be drawn between *spontaneous, induced* and *compulsory* participation. Spontaneous participation is based on local initiatives which have little or no external support and which from the very beginning have the capacity to be self-sustaining; induced participation, which is arguably more common, results from external initiatives seeking support or endorsement for external plans or projects; compulsory participation implies that people are mobilized or organized willy-nilly to undertake activities in which they have had no say and over which they have no control.

Similarly, forms of participation can be distinguished on the basis of whether they seek *cooperation* or promote *power-sharing*. Both forms involve interaction between the decision-makers and those affected by the decisions. In the former, the participants have a right to receive information, to submit protests, to make suggestions and to be consulted before final decisions are taken. In the latter, which is an intrinsically higher form of participation, the participants are conceded a share in formal power, varying from the right to impose temporary or permanent vetoes to the right to participate directly in decision-making. From this brief description it will be seen that very different forms of participation may emerge from the relations between those who decide and those who are affected by the decision.

It is impossible, therefore, to state categorically what exactly is meant by participation in rural development. Commentators have long been striving to lay down an exact definition, but a review of the literature reveals disagreement as to whether participation is essentially a *process*, a *programme*, a *technique* or a *methodology*. These four terms indicate the different approaches used in examining the concept.

The author's wish here is not to argue that one interpretation is better or more relevant than another, but to urge recognition of the variety of interpretations and, accordingly, of the need to examine the form of participation that is being practised. The evidence would suggest that no single form of participation is relevant to all situations and also that different forms have profoundly different consequences. A critical examination of the concept of participation should therefore be the first step in any attempt to bring CIH into operation (5).

12

Interpretations of CIH

A review of the literature on CIH reveals that, while there has been considerable discussion of community participation and many definitions of it have been suggested, few authors have attempted to define CIH. One study in fact has suggested that the concept of CIH is so riddled with equivocal terms such as 'self-reliance' and 'self-help' that a useful definition is almost impossible (6). Certainly there is widespread confusion and it is patently not possible to disentangle the concept of CIH from the variety of interpretations of community participation. CIH expresses the notion of local communities becoming involved in one particular development activity (i.e., health) and, while this might imply differences in approach and methods, the basic purpose will be the same.

It would perhaps be useful to start with a working definition of CIH and then attempt to adapt it to a variety of different contexts. In this respect the following definition of CIH in primary health care (7) would appear to be acceptable:

Community involvement [in health development] is a process by which partnership is established between the government and local communities in the planning, implementation and utilization of health activities in order to benefit from increased local self-reliance and social control over the infrastructure and technology of primary health care.

This is, on the one hand, a powerful statement of intent and, on the other, a political commitment with wide-ranging consequences. While it states the broad aim to be pursued, it also reveals an approach to participation in which the decisions are still a matter for professionals. There is little purpose, however, in trying to determine the precise implications of the definition; it is more important to discuss the issues raised by any commitment to CIH. The WHO inter-regional meeting in Brioni in 1985 examined the concept of CIH and suggested that there were two broad but distinct interpretations of the *practice* of CIH:

- CIH as *awareness* and *understanding* of health and health problems; and

- CIH as *access* to information and knowledge about health service programmes and projects.

The first interpretation lays stress on building up communities' awareness and understanding of the problems of health development and the causes of poor health as the basis for their future active involvement in health development. The second interpretation emphasizes that communities must have direct access to specific information and knowledge about health service programmes and projects as a pre-condition for becoming involved in health activities designed and to be directed by others.

Interpretations of CIH

(i) 'Participation . . . is simply involvement of a community in the administration and financing of a health service. Such involvement implies that the community participates . . . "in the planning, organization, operation and control of primary health care, taking the greatest possible advantage of local and national resources and other available resources" [Declaration of Alma-Ata].'

Agudelo, C. A. Community participation in health activities: some concepts and appraisal criteria. *Bulletin of the Pan American Health Organization*, **17**: 375–386 (1983).

(ii) 'Community involvement for health development is understood to refer to a *process* to establish participation between Government and local communities in the planning, implementation and use of health services in order to increase local self-reliance and social control over health care. Community involvement means that people, who have both the right and duty to participate in solving their own health problems, have greater responsibilities in assessing health needs, mobilising local resources and suggesting new solutions, as well as creating and maintaining local organizations.'

Activities of the WHO in promoting community involvement for health development. Unpublished WHO document, SHS/83.3.

(iii) 'Community participation is used loosely for different PHC activities which cut across the economic, learning and political spheres. While community activities in each of these spheres can contribute to improving the health conditions of poor people, they raise quite different issues, particularly as regards the organization of the ministry of health. The economic dimension of community participation dominates when community members contribute resources – materials, money, labour – to health-promoting activities, or when they are enlisted to carry out tasks delegated by the health care system: village health workers are a widespread example. In terms of learning, community participation is a two-way process involving both community members and health workers. When the community shares in defining needs, carrying out tasks, and gathering and processing information relevant to health, community members and health workers learn from each other. Finally, community participation is a political process in so far as community members acquire a say in decision-making about health and health care issues that affect them, and a measure of control over the persons that are supposed to serve their needs. Community participation in this sense raises the most serious organizational problems, and even dilemmas, for ministries of health.'

Strengthening ministries of health for primary health care. Geneva, World Health Organization, 1984 (WHO Offset Publication, No. 82), p. 39.

Within any particular country CIH must become a fundamental principle of the health delivery system. It cannot be merely a general characteristic of health service delivery: it must become the basic motive force of health activities. CIH is, however, ultimately linked to resources and there will be fundamental differences in practice between resource-rich and resource-poor countries. In resource-rich countries CIH has been essentially a response to consumer pressure and demand for better quality health services; in resource-poor countries it has mainly to do with coverage and increased access to basic health services.

The report on the Brioni meeting reviews the issues that have arisen as formal health services in different parts of the world have begun to adopt and implement the concept of CIH. It examines the concept and suggests its implications for health care practice; it suggests the changes that might be required in formal health services as a result of CIH; and finally it examines the relationship between CIH and traditional health care arrangements and practices. The regional and country reports presented at the Brioni meeting confirmed the complexity of the problems that arise as CIH is introduced into health services and health practice.

Comment

There is no shortage of literature seeking to explain the meaning of CIH or to determine and analyse the types of problem to which it gives rise. It would appear, however, that while there is a solid enough general commitment to CIH and a good understanding of what it means, there are still a number of aspects that require further and more thorough consideration:

(i) More detailed information is needed on the practice of CIH in different contexts, e.g., resource-rich/resource-poor, urban/ rural and capitalist economy/socialist economy countries or areas. CIH can only serve as an overall principle of health development; it cannot function merely on rhetoric, but needs to be tested and perfected in concrete situations. There is a case, therefore, for putting emphasis on practising CIH rather than on defining it. In this respect WHO should seek to promote and monitor the practice of CIH in different contexts in order to develop the understanding needed to support its practical application on a wider scale.

(ii) In respect of health development it is time to recognize more clearly that CIH is not an isolated phenomenon, but rather one aspect of a more general move towards ending the exclusion of the majority of the world's people from the development pro- cess. The emphasis should be put on linking-up community health workers with the activities of other sectors, such as adult education or rural extension, so that stress is laid on the process of participation and not merely on seeking to involve local people more directly in already established formal health ser- vices. There is much that the health sector must learn about the process of community participation in general before it seeks to incorporate that process into health development.

(iii) If CIH is to be fully applied, it will clearly have profound implications for formal health service practice. It would ap- pear, however, that these implications, e.g. a fundamental re- examination of both professional training and of the control of health programmes by health professionals, have not been given sufficient consideration and that the belief exists that CIH can merely be inserted into existing health services. It is perhaps time for a clear statement on the implications of CIH and the changes that will be required in formal health services if it is to be implemented. CIH involves a radical reorientation in the design and delivery of community health services, and the details of that reorientation need to be spelt out.

(iv) Ultimately the practice of CIH must receive constitutional and legal support if it is to operate effectively as a principle of health care and development. In this respect the experience of a number of European countries, such as Finland, may be useful (8). Ultimately, also, CIH can only flourish where governments

16

grant the basic right of local involvement and encourage local communities to assume the necessary responsibilities and powers.

(v) Finally there is the question of whether CIH must be of a different nature when used to deal with the symptoms of poor health or to deal with its causes. It is less difficult to use it to get local people to collaborate in the treatment and cure of a particular health problem. The approach must be somewhat different when CIH seeks to get local people involved in understanding the causes of their poor health and in finding effective solutions. There is, therefore, more than one approach to CIH and, indeed, the approach will be fundamentally different when it is solely the collaboration of local people that is sought rather than the development of their own abilities to tackle the causes of their poor health.

Community involvement in health care

Burma

The religious and sociocultural values and the political system in Burma embody the principles of community involvement as articulated in the declaration of Alma-Ata. Community involvement and participation are State policies in all aspects of development, including health. In the field of health development, successes have included sanitation campaigns, natural disaster relief, control of rat-induced plague epidemics, and mass smallpox vaccination: in each of these initiatives community participation was a vital component. Communities have also contributed to health development in other ways:

(a) direct community contributions to village health workers in order to replenish essential drugs and construct village health posts;

(b) voluntary labour for rural water supply projects, latrines and garbage pits;

(c) community participation, in the form of village people's councils, in the planning, organization, administrative supervision and control of primary health care activities.

Burma has found that the quality of performance of village health workers and their positive attitude and leadership are important factors in maintaining and sustaining community participation. Health authorities encourage and support new ideas from communities and health services staff alike and are keen where possible to provide resources for health initiatives that come from the communities.

El Zawahry, M. A. M. *Innovative approaches for increasing community involvement in the health care system.* WHO Regional Office for South-East Asia, unpublished document, SEA/HSD/111.

Peru

The present administration in Peru is committed to the democratization of the country's health services. Financial and human resources assigned to health services by the State are to be equitably allocated and, at the same time, the Peruvian people themselves are to be encouraged to participate in the management, supervision and control of health resources and services. In a recent policy statement on health development in the country, the Peruvian Government adopted the following among a series of policy guidelines:

(a) participation of organized communities in all the levels of the health system;

(b) effective decentralization of health services, with the delegation of authority to the peripheral level;

(c) development of new approaches to health problems, including the use of health technologies that can be applied by the people.

The policy statement adds that community participation is a difficult process to put into practice because the health system has traditionally worked apart from the people and their communal organizations. There is, therefore, a certain fear of community participation on the part of the people responsible for health service administration. The policy statement also sees decentralization in the health sector as a major challenge in a country with a historic tradition of centralization. In order to encourage this decentralization, 25 Departmental Health Units have been established having a Director and Deputy Director with the power of a Minister in the Department's geographical area. An interesting feature of this health sector decentralization is the holding of *jampinacuys* (group healing or group discussion on health issues). To date health is the only sector in the national administration in Peru to have achieved such a level of bureaucratic decentralization.

Peru, Ministry of Health, 1986.

References and notes

1. *Glossary of terms used in the "Health for All" Series, No. 1–8.* Geneva, World Health Organization, 1984 ("Health for All" Series, No. 9).

2. Lele, U. *The design of rural development.* Baltimore, MD, Johns Hopkins University Press, 1975.

3. Lisk, F. A. N. Popular participation in basic needs-orientated development planning. *Labour and society,* **6**: 3–14 (1981).

4. Pearse, A. & Stiefel, M. *Inquiry into participation: a research approach.* Geneva, United Nations Research Institute for Social Development, 1979.

5. For a fuller discussion of this range of interpretations see Oakley, P. & Marsden, D. *Approaches to participation in rural development.* Geneva, International Labour Office, 1985.

6. *Community participation and tropical disease control – an exercise in participatory research.* Unpublished WHO document, TDR/SER/SWG, 1983.

7. Fonaroff, A. *Community involvement in health systems for primary health care.* Unpublished WHO document, SHS/83.6.

8. Hastings, J. E. F. *An analysis of the nine-country study on forms of community participation in primary health care.* WHO Regional Office for Europe, unpublished document, ICP/PHC 013.2.

Chapter 3

Critical issues in CIH

The concept and practice of CIH are so broad and varied in nature that it is impossible to suggest a model of CIH that would be applicable to health care in all contexts. Countries such as China and the United States of America have long had mechanisms for community involvement but in the past five years or so CIH has become more systematically practised in many other countries. As more information emerges regarding CIH practice, it will become possible to determine the more important problems that arise when it is being put into effect. As has already been seen there have been a variety of interpretations of the concept itself and various degrees of commitment to it have been expressed. The essential point now is to obtain a better understanding of the main problems that arise when a health service seeks to implement CIH as a fundamental principle of its activities. In view of the increasing practice of CIH, it is now becoming possible to determine those problems and examine their implications.

The problems mentioned below were first discussed at the inter-regional meeting on CIH in Brioni; they have been the subject of further research and analysis since. They are not presented in any particular order of priority but rather in a logical sequence. The problems overlap, of course, and should be seen as a whole. For the purposes of this discussion, however, they will be examined individually and in some detail.

The community and CIH

CIH in practice not only involves health policy and health resources, but also the responsibilities and capabilities of the 'community'. Clearly, therefore, a study of CIH must begin with a thorough analysis of what the 'community' is that is supposed to play a part in a particular health programme or project. In this respect there is no shortage of anthropologically oriented studies in the developing world that describe the basic characteristics of urban and rural communities. What is still lacking, however, is empirical evidence of what aspects of communities are critical to their involvement in health development (*1*). Scrutiny of the more recent literature on CIH would suggest that those listed below are the most crucial.

(i) It is most important to know the exact nature of the community that is to become involved. The term 'community' is frequently used in development literature, although clearly there are different ideas of what it means. Psychologists, sociologists and anthropologists, for example, all use the term and are agreed in regarding it as more than a geographical expression. Current thinking on development is that the word is inadequate as a means of indicating people who share common needs and problems (*2*). Communities, in the geographical sense of the term, might contain a range of conflicting and competing groups and interests. For example, geographically defined communities can be divided in the first instance, into rich and poor, men and women, traditional and modern and so on. But even these divisions are too broad and a more precise differentiation will be needed between, for example, large landowners, small farmers and rural labourers or landowners and tenant-farmers. There is clearly a need to take into account economic and social differentiation in the community when health services are being provided at that level and particularly when an attempt is being made to involve the community in those services.

While some of the writings on CIH recognize the inadequacies of the term 'community', most seem to take it as some constant, static and uncomplicated unit, and concentrate on the weightier issues of health policy, structures for CIH and so on. Although this is clearly unsatisfactory, it may reflect a concern to convince those who control health systems of the importance of CIH. CIH will be quite meaningless in practice if 'community' continues to be used in an undifferentiated way for a geographically defined area. CIH must begin with a clear and unambiguous identification, based on economic and social criteria, of the people who constitute the 'community' and must seek to involve them in a way that is within their capabilities and is designed to solve problems that are relevant to them. CIH must be related to the specific situation of those whom it is seeking to involve.

In the absence for the moment of a more acceptable unit of economic and social organization for CIH, the author will continue to use the term 'community' in the text while recognizing its inadequacies and the need for a more soundly based method of dividing populations into their component parts.

(ii) An important aspect of CIH is the precise determination of what a community can contribute to health development; it is assumed that it will contribute according to its capabilities and resources. Already urban and rural communities contribute, in different ways in different countries, to providing and sustaining local health services (*3*). To understand the potential of community contributions to health development will involve a process of assessment, in which the communities will play a part, in order to determine what local capabilities and resources are available and in what way they can be built into health programmes and projects (*4*). More specifically local people's knowledge of health care and health practices should be ascertained and utilized. Essentially the practice of CIH recognizes that communities do have something to contribute, materially and intellectually, to the tackling of health problems and that it is necessary to determine what those contributions could be and to incorporate them in health practice. Also implicit in this approach to CIH is the recognition that communities will have their own views on health development and their own ideas on what the problems are (*5*).

(iii) In line with this more general analysis of people's participation, CIH must essentially be developed on the basis of some form of local organization. It is commonly acknowledged that organization is indispensable for providing ways and means of making participation possible (*6*). CIH too seeks for some form of organization at the community level that can act as the vehicle for involvement. Such an organization should:

- be local, indigenous and based on existing community structures and mechanisms;
- be created, where possible, as a result of local initiatives;
- be representative of the interests of the groups in the community whose involvement is being sought;
- be able to develop as a legitimate and formal representative body.

The issue of organization for CIH is very complex. It goes far beyond the mere establishment of a local structure such as a village health committee. It must be recognized, for example, that most

22

communities will have traditional mechanisms for participation. If the organization is to survive and be effective in encouraging people's involvement in health development, its establishment and development must be seen as an integral part of the process of CIH. In this respect strengthening district-level health systems for primary health care could be critically important in building up local organizations for CIH. Finally, those organizations will need the support of national legislation if they are to flourish and legitimately represent their members' interests.

(iv) In relation to the community's role in CIH, the term 'mobilization' is often used, referring to a radical and widespread process of collective organization and involvement which leads to local human and other resources being channelled into development efforts. In relation to health development, one author (7) has defined community mobilization as follows:

> Community mobilization is psychological, socio-cultural, political and economic training, retraining and redirection using relevant processes to create community awareness, understanding, motivation for the acceptance and the use of total community resources for planned collective changes or actions.

Clearly there is a strong case for linking the notion of mobilization to the concept of CIH. CIH will be of no use as a strategy if it is implemented in isolated, unconnected health programmes or projects. If CIH is to lead to more widespread and better health, widespread and sustained involvement will be needed. CIH must become a mass movement and the process of mobilization must become an integral part of the CIH process. There have already been examples of nationwide mobilization of people for health development and an attempt should be made to learn from them (8).

(v) As for the community in CIH, it may be wondered whether some communities might be more ready or able to get involved in health development than others. This is not an entirely novel question, since in other areas (e.g. agriculture), development workers classify communities and seek to determine which community characteristics are more favourable to development (9). Such an exercise, of course, must be treated with caution and should not be used alone to judge the ability of any particular community to become involved in health development. In particular it must be remembered that communities live in different political environments (e.g. democratic, authoritarian, centralized) which will largely determine the features of community participation. However, inquiries of this kind can at least provide a basis for assessing the potential for CIH and for building on what exists. With this in mind the following is a classification of communities in relation to CIH based upon research in the Americas (10):

Communities with some CIH	Communities with only cooperation and utilization of health services
(i) Urban and/or suddenly formed	(i) Rural and/or traditional
(ii) Consensus that health is a priority need	(ii) Consensus that health needs are satisfied and that other problems have greater priority
(iii) Social cohesion/sense of common interest	(iii) Social, economic or political divisions; apathy
(iv) History of successful community action	(iv) Community action non-existent or one-time only

Such a range of favourable and unfavourable characteristics begs a whole series of questions, but also singles out some characteristics that are important for successful CIH. However, terms such as 'consensus', 'social cohesion' 'divisions' and 'apathy' will have to be clearly defined, their interpretation depending on the analytical criteria used by the author concerned. They must be examined objectively, not subjectively. 'Consensus' and 'cohesion' are vital to CIH but they must be real and based on commonly accepted criteria and not merely reflect casual agreement at the community level. The basis of involvement is solidarity, but that solidarity must be more than community consensus on the importance of health problems (11).

Interestingly the Americas study suggests that urban communities are generally more prepared for CIH than their 'traditional' rural counterparts. In the Americas this is not surprising, in view of the increasing urbanization of the American continent and the presence of health services mainly in urban areas. Certainly urban communities in the Americas, for a variety of reasons, such as access to information or a greater degree of politicization, are usually in a better position to become usefully involved in development activities. On the other hand, the reverse is probably true in other parts of the world such as Africa, where more people live in rural areas.

Furthermore, in countries that have undergone a period of internal structural reform and where communities have been mobilized and organized for development, the question of the 'readiness' of communities may not be relevant. In these situations it is more appropriate to ask whether the health service bureaucracy has failed to keep up with structural changes that have laid the basis for community involvement. In such situations, if CIH is not beginning to develop, it is perhaps due to the failings of the health service and not the unreadiness of local communities.

The community

Convincing Nepalese villagers to support and participate in development projects often makes it necessary for field workers to bring together disparate individuals in pursuit of a common goal. "Who is the community?" asked the adviser of an education project. "It is a fallacy to think there are unified communities. In every one you have divisions and in some you have active fighting."

This is echoed by the UNICEF Project Officer: "All the way down to the basic level you have divisions. Only when you get to a cluster of houses do you have a sense of community. This kind of fragmented community will be a big problem in any project."

The process of bringing members of a community together in pursuit of a project involves winning over local leaders, providing an immediate benefit of some kind and establishing a good reputation, often by word-of-mouth assurance from relatives and acquaintances in the neighbouring areas that the project is effective.

"Take the case of the water supply," remarked a UNICEF field worker. "In the beginning it wasn't easy. People didn't know about clean water; at first when we asked them to dig trenches and carry pipes, we had problems. Now people know about water supply and there is really strong community participation."

Communities are now expected to do more than dig trenches. "The idea that people used to have about community participation was that it's free labour," said the Project Officer. "But

community participation actually means meetings which involve people in as many decisions as they're capable of
handling – decisions such as 'Do we want a water tap?' or
'Where should the taps be?' or 'How should we organize the
labour?' "

The experience of water supply projects has pushed back
barriers to widespread community participation in Nepal. The
water supply programmes have become anchored in local
choice – with district assemblies forwarding lists of water
needs which they have received from village assemblies.

Felsenthal, M. Who is the community? *UNICEF News*, No. 124, pp. 26–27 (1986).

Support mechanisms for CIH

It is commonly agreed that CIH cannot be instituted and
developed without the support of appropriate mechanisms at different levels. Such mechanisms can exist and operate at both national
and community level and are indispensable for the process of CIH.
The evidence to date suggests that in countries where CIH has
begun to develop, it has done so with the assistance of a variety of
support mechanisms.

The literature on CIH emphasizes the key role of support
mechanisms and puts forward suggestions, sometimes detailed, on
what those mechanisms should be and how they should function
(*12*). Support mechanisms for CIH are described both at the national and at the local level and inevitably the relationship between
mechanisms at the two levels becomes a serious problem. In the first
instance, however, it is important to establish what factors can affect
the CIH mechanisms either favourably or adversely. Many writers
single out the critical factors and argue that support mechanisms for
CIH will be inoperable unless those factors are favourable. The
factors are broad in scope and are invariably described in general
terms. The following is a composite list of the factors considered to
be of critical importance if a support mechanism for CIH is to
succeed:

(i) *Political commitment to CIH.* This is probably the most fundamental support for the CIH process, since it will determine
the success of such important mechanisms as decentralization.
The political commitment, not just to CIH but to the whole

process of participation, is indispensable for creating the conditions favourable to increasing involvement. Where there is no political commitment, community involvement will not only not flourish but may even be deliberately hindered.

(ii) *Reorientation of the bureaucracy in support of CIH.* The administrative support required for effective CIH will only materialize when the government bureaucracy is reoriented to support the process. Classically bureaucracies are designed to pass down policy and information and are inflexible. CIH will never flourish until bureaucratic structures radically reorient their procedures and behaviour.

(iii) *Development of capacity for self-management.* CIH will not function unless action is taken to build up the organizational and management abilities of local people. CIH, therefore, does not rely merely on the communication of new ideas on health care, but must also develop local ability to assume full responsibility for such care.

(iv) *Minimum basic health structure and coverage.* CIH cannot be implemented unless there is at least a minimum health care infrastructure, fairly widespread access to health services, and national and local financial resources to support those services. There have to be health activities in which local people can become involved. CIH is not therefore a realistic strategy for all areas of the world; it is more immediately relevant to those areas that possess a minimum infrastructure of health services.

Probably not all health administrators or workers would agree that the above are the most essential support factors for CIH. Certainly they are not suggested as a model relevant to all situations, but more as representative of factors that have emerged from the practice of CIH. There is general agreement, however, that the factors listed imply formidable changes, and that may be the most important single reason why CIH in many countries is much talked of but little practised. Political commitment and bureaucratic reorientation, for example, are not changes that can or will occur at the drop of a hat. And yet without the radical changes implicit in such factors, CIH becomes an extremely limited concept. It is unwise to underestimate the magnitude of the structural changes that will be required to create the effective support necessary for CIH and without which CIH will function only within the limited confines of single health programmes or projects.

Ethiopia: The structure of national participation

In late 1974 the Provisional Military Administrative Council (PMAC) declared Ethiopia a socialist state, stressing equality, self-reliance, the dignity of labour and the supremacy of the common good. Emphasis was laid on the need to socialize the means of production so as to eliminate the causes of class differentiation and to promote the country's productive forces. In March 1975, a land reform was proclaimed and all rural land was declared the common property of the Ethiopian people. Immediately an effort began to organize the peasants for the part they were expected to play. In December 1975, a proclamation established the peasants' associations which were to be the main vehicle of peasant involvement. Women's associations were also established by the PMAC to represent and promote the interests of rural women in Ethiopia.

In Ethiopia greater peasant participation was the cornerstone of the revolutionary process. In the first year the PMAC launched an offensive to make contact with the rural masses and to begin the process of involving them in the revolutionary transformation. Within a short time, thousands of peasants' associations had been formed. Peasant participation was expressed in such terms as 'collectivization' and later 'co-operativization' as the PMAC sought to institutionalize a communal form of agriculture.

The process of peasant participation was presented as evolutionary and was governed by three basic principles: voluntary participation, mutual benefits and the strict application of democratic centralism. The key word, of course, is the 'voluntary' nature of the participation, implying that the peasants had the choice of whether to support the process of collectivization or not. Essentially the approach was to begin by establishing some basic forms of participation (i.e. peasants' associations) which would lead to some kind of higher form with widespread collectivization of production. The peasants' world was in fact turned upside down overnight. Previously they had been totally excluded from any form of involvement in the development of the Ethiopian State (apart from those few who had become involved in capitalist development programmes) but now they were being asked to participate actively in the socialist revolution.

In this process of developing and institutionalizing local participation, the PMAC used two basic means:

(i) the *Zemacha*: the mobilizátion of secondary school and university students to spread throughout the country, make contact with the peasant communities and prepare the ground for participation.

(ii) *peasants' associations*: considered as the lowest administrative unit of the State, these were expected to coordinate administrative functions, agitate, and mobilize the people to participate in political and economic activities and maintain the security of their region.

The *Zemacha* and the peasants' associations made the first impact upon a peasantry that had been subjected to feudal isolation for centuries. Since this first impact, and particularly since 1979, the emphasis has been upon agricultural collectivization and the developing of cooperatives as the basis for continued peasant involvement. Although as yet there have been few detailed studies of how this process of institutionalized participation is evolving, the Ethiopian experience remains one of the few contemporary examples of a national structure for people's participation.

Oakley, P. & Marsden, D. *Approaches to participation in rural development*, Geneva, International Labour Office, 1985, pp. 54–58.

The above comments notwithstanding, it must be assumed that the political commitment to CIH will be forthcoming and consideration must be given to what support mechanisms could be important. Before particular mechanisms are mentioned, however, the practice of CIH to date suggests a number of basic principles which should govern the establishment and functioning of such mechanisms (*13*):

● CIH implies partnership between health services and their professionals and local community people. Only genuine partnership ensures a proper compromise between the views of government and local people.

● CIH is based on individual and collective leadership at the community level. Support mechanisms, therefore, must not be implanted from outside, but should be built into and be part of leadership patterns and structures at the community level.

● CIH must be sustainable. The mechanisms established to support CIH, particularly at the community level, must be realistic and sustainable under local conditions. It is no good establishing mechanisms such as administrative structures that cannot be sustained locally and can only function with external assistance.

● While existing and traditional practices of community coopera- tion and health care are important as a basis for CIH, organiza- tional support structures should be new and innovative. CIH is a radically new concept of health practice and demands new structures if it is to be put to practical effect.

CIH practice to date, therefore, suggests that the above are useful principles. It must be stressed, however, that they do not constitute a model applicable to all contexts, but should be used as a guide to the kinds of criteria that will be important in developing support mechanisms for CIH.

The country reports presented to the inter-regional meeting at Brioni showed that where CIH had begun to develop, a certain number of specific support mechanisms had been used at national level which seemed to be vital to the CIH process, although empha- sis naturally varied from country to country. Of these national support mechanisms, the following would appear to be, by common consensus and in order of priority, the most important.

Decentralization

More has been written about the need for administrative de- centralization for effective CIH than about any other support mecha- nism. Such decentralization, of course, is not only important for health development; it is also recognized as a vital factor in stimu- lating all local development (*14*). It ensures that there is a flow of information, resources, decisions and action between the national government at the centre and the localities; it encourages inter- sectoral coordination in the localities, reduces excessive reliance on the central government and promotes local initiative and respon- sibility. One study (*8*) argued the importance of decentralization for primary health care as follows:

In efforts to promote greater control of resources and their distribution by those whom the PHC strategy is supposed to help, the decentralization of administrative and decision- making functions has been widely proposed. It is seen as vital both in terms of efficiency, as decisions can be made at local level without involving complex and time-consuming national bureaucracies, and in terms of the political devolution of power, making the administrative and distributional network

30

more answerable to the people. Logically, as PHC is seen as 'peripheral' care, the political structures affecting it should be closer to the periphery, thus enabling communities to enter and influence them.

While few would disagree with that statement, the enormous problems entailed in seeking to bring about administrative decentralization must not be underestimated, particularly since bureaucracies do not normally willingly delegate their authority. Essentially, administrative decentralization will only be of value if it is part of a radical reorientation of the bureaucratic machinery at the national level. However, once the central authorities are committed to decentralization, the following considerations should be borne in mind:

- There must be a local administration strong and capable enough to assume the duties and powers delegated by central authorities.

- If it is to be effective decentralization must be accompanied by a shift of resources to the localities.

- Care must be taken to avoid local political élites being able to use the delegated powers for their own ends.

- The decentralization of administrative functions must be accompanied by the decentralization of political power; otherwise it will result in increased interference by the central government in local affairs.

There are a number of reasons why the decentralization of health services may be useful. In many large countries, for example, regional differences often demand different health policies and approaches. It is important for regional and local health authorities to be able to adapt health policies to varying local conditions whether ecological, social or cultural. Decentralization also helps promote local decision-making and participation and ensures that the health services are more accountable to the people they are supposed to serve. In respect of health development, decentralization is a matter not only of efficiency but also of control (*15*).

Decentralization in support of CIH cannot be divorced from decentralization in support of development in general. In some European countries varying degrees of decentralization have already occurred and have been supported by appropriate legislation (*16*).

31

Senegal: Health service decentralization

In 1972, Senegal carried out a reform of its regional and local administrative structure based on three principles: decentralization, devolution and participation. Decentralization in Senegal has meant giving organized communities the authority they need if they are to take the greatest possible responsibility for their own destiny. Its value lies in the fact that it "brings government closer to the governed" and above all allows people to take responsibility for their own welfare within the framework of the State system.

In 1979 the Ministry of Public Health was reorganized in the same spirit. In 1980, and after trials in several project areas, community involvement in public health was put into general effect. As a basis for this involvement health committees were made responsible for making use of local health resources and facilities. In July 1980, the Ministry published an explanatory handbook entitled 'Community involvement in public health: principles and guidelines'. In February 1982, regional public health services were established. In the same year, following regular meetings between health officials and the regional committees, Senegal produced its first health plan. Among the obstacles to the policy of decentralization that were encountered were:

● opposition by health personnel;
● lack of qualified staff to implement the administrative reforms;
● lack of management skills at the regional level.

Public health administration in Senegal has undergone several changes as part of the reorganization of the national administration. The main changes include:

(a) the division of the health system into 5 levels, forming a pyramidal structure ranging from primary care services up to the national authorities;

(b) the strengthening of administrative coordination at the different levels;

(c) the systematic development of the health committees, which have become the channel through which people can influence the activities of the health system.

Decentralization also has an important effect on multisectoral activities. Contacts with other departments give local health services access to a larger pool of resources and NGOs have become better integrated into health programmes. In short, decentralization enables better coordination between the health services and other local groups in carrying out health activities.

With the advent of decentralization, CIH is no longer merely an empty slogan in Senegal. Problems, however, still exist, particularly in relation to the funding of recurrent expenditure and the shortage of qualified personnel. The decentralization of health services to the localities has led to problems in regard to the resources and staff available locally; those problems are still being resolved. The Senegalese experience shows that the decentralization of health services is inconceivable without an overall policy of decentralization. Senegal's primary health care programme, however, which was started in 1978, has undoubtedly benefited from the national policy of decentralization and the setting-up of regional structures for devolution of authority to lower levels.

Adapted from Ndiaye, J. M. Decentralization of the health services in Senegal. In: Mills, A. et al., ed. *Decentralization and health-for-all strategy* (Geneva, World Health Organization (in press)). This publication contains ten country case studies on decentralization of health services.

In most parts of the world, however, there has been almost no decentralization in the shape of the devolution of effective authority and power to the localities. For that reason, when certain health programmes or projects seek to encourage local structures and organizations in support of CIH, the initiative is confined to the health programme or project concerned and not part of a more general transformation of the civil administration. In most countries effective decentralization in support of CIH must await a more general movement towards decentralization of the administration, which will not be spontaneous but will have to be achieved by pressure from below. In the few cases where decentralization has taken place and the conditions for local involvement have been created (e.g. Ethiopia and the United Republic of Tanzania) it could be argued that the health services have not taken advantage of the situation and have not promoted CIH as effectively as they could have done.

Effective administrative decentralization is particularly important for a health strategy of developing health systems at the district level. The current emphasis on district health systems, with its concern to promote community involvement at the district level, is dependent upon decentralization to district level of health service responsibilities for such things as planning, manpower development and financial control. Clearly, however, the decentralization required is not limited to the health sector but is a major political issue. It is argued that effective development of district health systems will require appropriately trained staff at the district level and planning and advisory support from the central health structure. Although equity, accessibility, prevention and intersectoral coordination are also important factors in developing district health systems, it is difficult to resist the view that effective administrative decentralization is the key issue.

Local structures

The need for appropriate local structures to support CIH is generally recognized, although ideas on how to set them up often differ widely. Some argue that the existing network of local structures should be the basis for CIH, others that CIH demands new thinking and the development of new structures (17). Similarly some advocate letting appropriate structures arise spontaneously in the localities while others believe in making use of already proven structures, such as local health committees. Furthermore it is difficult to conceive of effective local structures which would confine themselves to health matters alone. A local structure with the power and authority to manage resources and determine priorities will be unlikely to deal exclusively with health development. Indeed it could be argued that such structures must have wider responsibilities if they are to avoid becoming parochial and treating health problems in isolation from other problems of development.

Where local structures are developed in support of CIH, a number of problems arise in relation to the community:

- Consideration of how to support CIH should begin by determining what existing local structures (e.g. traditional groups or local health committees) could provide a basis for any future innovative structures. Building upon what already exists is a useful principle in developing structures for CIH.

- The initiative and pressure for developing local support structures must come from below. The imposition of structures from above is contrary to the principles of CIH.

- The relationship between the formal health services and the local health structure is of critical importance; it must not be one of dependence. The local health structure should be able to work on its own without direct intervention by the formal health services.

- Criteria should be laid down for membership of local structures in support of CIH to ensure that they are truly representative and cannot be taken over by local elites.

In developing local structures in support of CIH much can be learnt from initiatives covering other fields in addition to health (*18*). One characteristic common to the vast majority of poor people in the world is their lack of organization and hence their lack of influence on development. The building-up of popular organizations has therefore become a priority of many development projects. Local organizations are essential to the process of participation but although they need support and guidance they should be allowed to evolve in their own way and should represent the interests of a clearly defined group. The evidence suggests that such organizations do not flourish and do not serve authentically as a basis for participation if they are imposed by a bureaucratic decision from above, unless the decision is part of a wider structural reform (*19*).

Developing local organizations: the Philippines

Sarilakas (a word derived from a Tagalog phrase meaning "own strength", i.e. "self-reliance"), funded by the International Labour Organisation and the Dutch government, is a transformation of an earlier project launched in 1980 to encourage rural workers to undertake group economic activities, with external loans and technical assistance.

Grass-roots organizations had been formed. However, they remained passive, waiting for finance and deliveries from above which had been promised but failed to materialize. The orientation of the project changed radically when the people were encouraged to determine for themselves their problems and priorities and decide what they would like to do.

In one village, poor tenant farmers and fishermen revamped their organization and turned towards predominantly economic goals – taking a production loan from the bank under group liability, developing a collective savings fund and buying a hand tractor. In another village, similar economic activities were combined with pressure on the authorities to implement land-reform laws providing for a change from share-cropping to leaseholding. In a third village, in addition to undertaking collective production of mangoes, the poor rural workers, becoming aware of their rights, succeeded in having forest land, previously forcibly withheld, allocated to them according to law. In another area, sugar-cane farmers formed an organization to fight a court case to force landowners to reduce fees for transporting their produce to the mills.

In an evaluation of Sarilakas carried out in July 1982 individual members were asked what each considered to be his or her greatest gain from the project. Without a single exception, they replied that the greatest benefit was educational: first, they had acquired knowledge of their legal rights as workers, and second, they had come to realize that those rights could be enforced only if they became organized. Even those who had made considerable economic gains in the shape of higher incomes from the collective economic efforts, put the educational benefit first. After two years of pilot experimentation Sarilakas is poised to expand. Poor communities in other areas are asking for help in setting up similar organizations.

In this case also the initiators of the project have set up a non-governmental entity by the name of PROCESS (Participatory Research and Organization of Community through Education and Self-Help Services) in order to work outside the government bureaucracy with the utmost possible independence.

From: The greatest benefit was educational. *UNICEF News*, No. 124, p. 9 (1986).

Local intersectoral cooperation

There are strong arguments in favour of more effective local intersectoral cooperation in support of CIH. They stress the need for a holistic view of health problems and the need to avoid a rigidly sectoral approach to their solution. The lack of intersectoral cooperation is not, of course, limited to health issues; it plagues all development efforts. The Declaration of Alma-Ata, for example, mentioned intersectoral cooperation as a fundamental condition for local health development. It is a question not only of cooperation between the health services and other services working in development, but also, and more important, of cooperation within the different levels of the health services. In this respect the lack of a comprehensive health plan was seen in many instances as the cause of the lack of health sector cooperation.

It must be recognized, however, that local intersectoral cooperation is not only not very common but, as with the other support mechanisms already mentioned, depends essentially on a more general reorientation of administrative practice. Research in the Americas, for example, found that effective local cooperation in support of CIH existed in only one country, Cuba (*10*). Regional and country reports presented at the Brioni meeting also confirmed the widespread lack of local intersectoral cooperation in support of CIH. In these circumstances it is appropriate to reaffirm the importance of local intersectoral cooperation and to suggest that, in the first place, emphasis should be put on better coordination within the various levels of the health services. There would seem to be little purpose in promoting intersectoral coordination if such coordination is lacking inside the health system itself. In addition, if the health sector has adopted the notion of local involvement, as local health structures emerge they should take the initiative in promoting better intersectoral coordination.

Another form of intersectoral cooperation is collaboration between the different departments and ministries whose activities are related in any way to health. Many factors—food, education, environmental conditions and employment opportunities—influence people's health, and collaboration between the departments concerned is highly important. It is, of course, more difficult since it involves a number of different administrative entities but it is a form of cooperation that will influence the effectiveness of health care. (*15*).

Logistic support

As a continuing process, CIH will need periodic and timely logistic support. In many countries CIH will require new local arrangements for providing it with the support it needs. This, of course, applies not only to the health sector, but to all innovations in development. However, logistic support for CIH will raise a number of problems:

●   How much support can be provided will very much depend upon the state of development of the local infrastructure.

●   Logistic support for CIH must be based on what already exists and not make new demands on scarce resources.

●   Logistic support for CIH should be based wherever possible on existing resources within local communities, such as local means of communication.

Nongovernmental organizations (NGOs) and CIH

In different parts of the world, national and international NGOs have gained considerable experience in health care and health development. In relation to supporting CIH, NGOs have certain advantages over governments. They tend to be less bound by red tape and bureaucratic procedures; they are usually staffed by the type of people likely to support CIH ideologically; and, given the increasing volume of resources they command, they can often make substantial contributions to health programmes. Similarly NGOs almost invariably work on a small scale and are therefore more closely involved in the localities and more able to work in practice with a concept like CIH. Since they are not government-controlled, they are often able to promote local initiatives that can generate their own momentum for development rather than coming to depend on external support.

It is widely recognized that NGOs can play an important role in supporting CIH. One study suggests that in the health field NGOs are particularly useful as 'brokers', helping local communities plan and implement health programmes and linking them up with government programmes (20). More important, NGOs' support can be most useful as local health structures and plans emerge and as attempts are made to introduce the CIH concept into health service thinking. NGOs can thus make an important contribution to CIH but a number of issues may arise:

- Governments should recognize and support the work of NGOs in health development.

- NGOs should not attempt to replace formal health structures but should correlate their health work with them.

- In regard to community involvement in health, NGOs should not duplicate what is being done by the formal health services but should play a more educational role.

This is not the place to list the considerations arising from NGO involvement, not just in health care, but in development projects generally. In many ways NGOs represent an alternative to the frequently centrally planned and tightly controlled development approach of governments, but even NGO-supported development initiatives have their problems. Many NGOs, however, have supported initiatives seeking to develop the basis of community involvement on a wider scale and are accordingly more ideologically in tune with the operational demands of CIH (21).

NGOs and CIH: the Klampok Programme, Indonesia

The Klampok programme began in a rural area in 1973. It was based on principles of community development which regard health as only one component in the improvement of village life and made use of the experience of Dr Gunawan Nugroho who had participated in the internationally acclaimed Solo programme. It initially covered the village of Klampok, with a population of about 5000 people. Unique in that it had close integration with and the support of the Regency government, it was later extended to serve the entire Purworejo-Klampok subdistrict, which had a population of about 32 000. Later still, the model was extended to cover the entire Regency. Its staff was about 20 people. The programme was community-based, emphasizing health as only one aspect of village improvement, which also included agriculture, communications, nutrition and education. The health component was service-oriented, providing both for service extension by the use of community health workers and a health insurance scheme, *dana sehet,* which provided participants with funds to cover both consultations with doctors and medicines. (It did not cover hospital expenses.)

Originally the programme was developed by the medical staff in consultation with community workers. However, the programme director, a doctor, dissatisfied with this approach, began to seek ways of gaining greater community participation in the programme. Efforts were made to establish community responsibility for both activities and funds. Community health workers became responsible to a village committee. A health insurance scheme was established by which the village committee collected and administered the surplus funds which were used for building up community income-generating activities. The role of the medical professional changed from that of prime planner to that of resource person. The medical people continued to treat patients at the clinic and act as consultants to the community health programme when asked to do so. The community development workers advised the medical professionals how to develop the programme and train community health workers. The role of community health workers was both to provide services and to act as agents for change. Volunteers selected by the community committee did first-aid work, simple prevention, sanitation and general simple community development work. Their training em-

phasized both health and disease care as well as the organizational and communication skills they needed in their community development tasks.

Finance for the Klampok programme began with US $25 000 for
a rural clinic and government provision of a stimulation fund of
about US $500 per village as well as a training fund in the same
amount. Through a special committee the Government also
allocated funds and provided some health services. Community support for the programme came through the health
insurance schemes and the community health workers.

Rifkin, S. B. Primary health care in Southeast Asia: attitudes about community
participation in community health programmes. *Social science and medicine*,
17 (19): 1489–1496 (1983).

Comment

Any discussion of the support mechanisms required for CIH
must objectively take into account the enormous changes that will be
required in present health service delivery and practice to develop
an environment in which CIH can become a reality. It is generally
agreed that the process of CIH needs support mechanisms if it is to
develop and function and that it would be no use proclaiming CIH
in places where support is not available or is unlikely to materialize
in the short term. At least a minimum of health infrastructure must
exist therefore, before the development of CIH can be contem-
plated. Similarly CIH must not be divorced from any general process
of increasing participation that might be taking shape in a particular
country; health services should fit into existing movements towards
participation and not seek unnecessarily to develop structures to
serve health development alone. Finally, in areas where the required
minimum infrastructure for the support of CIH exists, the following
sequence should be observed:

Political commitment:	(i) Increasing resources allocated to the localities	(ii) Backing for local structures in support of CIH
↓ Decentralization:	(i) Development of local infrastructure	(ii) Logistic support

Education and training for CIH

CIH is not an approach to health care and development that
can be merely proclaimed and fitted into an existing health pro-

gramme. Like participation in general, CIH differs substantially from conventional health practice and theoretical and practical knowledge of it will have to be spread by means of the health services. Those services will, therefore, have to be educated to understand CIH and their staffs trained to put it into practice. Both activities are indispensable to the widespread adoption of CIH and involve not only informally disseminating limited information but incorporating CIH into existing education and training activities or even, where appropriate, radically reorienting those activities to take account of CIH.

The Brioni meeting confirmed that the present situation in countries with regard to progress in education and training for CIH was not encouraging and that there was still much to be done (*22*). Although there are a number of examples of innovations in the training of health service staff for CIH promotion so far little substantial change seems to have taken place in health service training to reflect a commitment to CIH (*23*). The meeting recognized that most health workers are the products of deeply entrenched medical systems and only a major reorientation in training could effectively integrate CIH into those systems. In considering the current situation regarding training for CIH, the Brioni meeting argued that CIH must pervade all levels of health training and drew particular attention to a number of points:

(i) Where training for CIH is being undertaken it is usually at the lower levels of the health service. It is important, however, that it should take place at all levels, from senior staff to members of the community so as to ensure widespread preparation for CIH.

(ii) Even where there is a commitment to CIH at the higher levels in the health services, it can often not be translated into practice owing to a lack of formal training.

(iii) So far, few health services seem to have provided either the resources or the time for training in CIH.

(iv) The appropriate content of training for CIH has still to be determined. In this respect the balance of the training content for CIH is a critical issue; most medical training concentrates on transferring medical knowledge, while training for CIH requires the passing on of knowledge drawn from other subjects, such as the social sciences.

Few would dispute that education and training are fundamental to CIH if it is to become an integral part of health practice or that the above points summarize the main problems in this respect. However, there has been a frustrating lack of experimentation on how education and training for CIH can best be integrated into health services. Little has been written on education and training specifically for CIH. Health services are only just beginning to consider CIH and its implications and a period of research and experimentation will be required before the most appropriate content and methods of education and training for CIH can be determined.

It is generally accepted, however, that education and training for CIH should be considered at three levels—professional staff, community health workers, community leaders—so that content and methods can be related to the differing roles and responsibilities of professionals and members of communities at the national, regional and district levels.

Professional staff

There is little evidence that, apart from explanatory documents, public statements of commitment and attendance at national and international meetings, any substantial action has yet been taken towards systematically preparing senior health staff for CIH. Any such preparation will therefore have to start more or less from scratch.

Of course, senior health staff will not be concerned with the day-to-day practice of CIH, so that their education and training will be different from that of colleagues at other levels. Some would argue, however, that the senior professional level is the critical level for education and training in CIH, since if those who determine policy and allocate resources do not do so on the basis of CIH, staff at lower levels will lack the support required to implement it. Unfortunately no outline of a CIH training programme for senior professional staff can be given here since there are few examples to serve as a guide. Training at this level presents particular problems, not the least being the difficulty of convincing senior staff that they require further training at all. It also raises a number of issues:

(i)   Since most senior professional staff are doctors, should training for CIH begin in formal medical education? Such a decision could imply radical changes in medical education which might be resisted by the professional bodies concerned.

(ii) Training at this level would probably put more emphasis on theory than practice. Senior staff need to understand more the essence of CIH and its implications for the health services than the details of its practical application.

(iii) During their training, however, senior staff should have adequate opportunities for studying the conditions at lower levels in the health services under which community involvement in health would be taking place.

It is difficult to resist a feeling of unreality when linking the notion of training in CIH with senior staff. Training implies the transfer of knowledge and skills in order to change or improve performance. It could be argued that the essentially conservative and authoritarian nature of higher medical training throughout the world has a built-in anti-CIH orientation, with its emphasis on professional knowledge and the delivery of health care. In the circumstances it is difficult to imagine the concept of CIH, in its full sense, having much impact at this level without prior radical changes in the structure and orientation of the health services. Although there is evidence from some countries (e.g., China and Cuba) that such changes do succeed in modifying the thinking of senior professional staff, there is still a lot to learn about how to change the attitudes of senior staff in formal health services towards CIH in the Western countries. It is not simply a question of public commitment or statements of policy; it requires a major reorientation in the formulation of policy and in the systems and practices of health care.

Community health workers

The person who will be most directly involved in the practice of CIH is the community (or village) health worker (CHW or VHW). The Inter-Regional Conference on Community Health Workers held in Cameroon in December, 1986, confirmed the vital role of the CHW in promoting community participation and advocated more relevant training (24). Similarly a recent study examining the crucial role of the CHWs as primary health care leaders stressed that an important part of their work is the promotion of community involvement (25). There is therefore widespread acceptance of the crucial role of the community health workers in promoting CIH.

It is among CHWs that practical knowledge of CIH is most important, since it is at that level that CIH ceases to be a concept or a policy and becomes a way of practising health care. In formal health services, therefore, it is at that level that the emphasis should be put on training for CIH. Considerable thought has already been given to the general training of CHWs and there is no shortage of literature to serve as a guide (26–28). Most of the literature, however, concentrates on the medical aspects of the CHW's training and as yet there is little soundly based experience on what would constitute relevant training in CIH for a CHW (29). A recent authoritative study on community health workers, for example, while providing an admirable review of a number of important issues, offers little guidance on how CHWs might be trained to promote CIH effectively (24).

In view of the critical role of the CHW in CIH and the present emphasis in CHW training on medical matters, the question is how best CHWs can be trained to use their medical knowledge in a CIH approach to health care. The issues involved, which are inextricably linked, include the following:

(i)   What essentially is the role of a CHW? Is the CHW specifically an extender of health services or, more generally, an agent of change with particular concern for health care and development. In this respect we must distinguish between the *service* and the *developmental* functions of the CHW. Both of these functions are important and the balance between them in practice will depend upon the demands of the local setting.

(ii) What is the appropriate balance between the various components of training for CIH? For the moment no conclusive answer can be given to this question, in the absence of evidence derived from practice. The balance is bound to be influenced by our conception of the role of the CHW . An extender of health services would presumably require training that emphasized medical knowledge, whereas an agent of change would need training in more general knowledge and skills related to community development processes.

(iii) When is it best to train a CHW for CIH? Training for CIH requires the learning of medical knowledge and of participatory skills and which of the two should come first is a moot point. Practical experience in other areas of development, such as agricultural extension work, would suggest that the training in basic technical skills should be given first, followed by training in participatory skills. This seems to be the logical sequence and would avoid the confusion that could be caused by an attempt to train a CHW in both aspects at the same time.

(iv) What form of training in CIH is most appropriate for a CHW? Although no evidence is available from the health sector, experience in other sectors can be considered, which suggests

44

that training in participatory skills should comprise a period of structured training, later supported by periodic courses or seminars to ensure that CHWs are kept abreast of changing skills or developments in participation.

The interlinked issues just listed offer some guidance on how to proceed. In regard to the first two points mentioned, it could be argued that CIH implies that a CHW is not just an extender of health services but essentially an agent seeking to promote change in the health sector. The distinction is crucial, since it determines the basic orientation of the CHW. As an extender of health services a CHW would be more concerned with, for example, communicating established health policy, delivering health services to the community and providing curative medical care. A CHW as an agent of change would be more concerned with developing local people's abilities to understand health problems and plan activities to deal with them and also with building up a basis for more sustained local involvement in health development. An agent of change would also take a wider view of the basis of health development (e.g. links with agricultural development) and have a greater concern for preventive activities.

It is not yet possible to determine conclusively the content of CIH training for a community health worker. It is possible, however, to begin to determine the key aspects of the non-medical content of such training:

Understanding community involvement	– an examination of the concept, its interpretation, the way it can be given practical effect and its implications for health development.
Communities and their organization	– basic sociological and anthropological theories and an analysis of communities and their internal dynamics and structures.
Processes and methods of communication	– the theories and practice of communication in the development process.
Working with groups	– the techniques and skills of working with small groups by developing group awareness and ability to take and implement development decisions.

This general outline, of course, needs considerable refinement and definition before a specific training course can be designed. It is presented here to suggest the main non-medical elements of training for CIH that would follow and support training in more formal, medical matters (*30*). The most important point, however, is that whatever its content, training for CIH should be participatory. A participatory approach would help CHWs to learn how CIH should work in practice.

The community health worker (CHW) and CIH

Thailand

Community participation is a prominent feature of the community health worker programme in Thailand. Since 1979 primary health care has been part of a national development plan. Community health workers, village health communicators, and village health volunteers carry out service functions and are also involved in development. A stage has been reached at which the village system of health care is a self-managed community primary health care system. Self-reliance is fostered through strong community organization, mobilization of resources, and financial management and manpower deployment. The developed villages are presented as models and there is technical cooperation among villages for disseminating information on effective practices. By analogy with technical cooperation at the international level, this is referred to as TCDV (technical cooperation among developing villages). The village development committee is a multisectoral organization that supports the community health worker and itself receives strong support from the higher levels of the administration for rural development.

China

The concept of the community health worker is similar in all parts of China. Community health workers have service and development functions, which they carry out in an integrated manner, and fulfil a bridging role between the health sector and the community. Their skills in mobilizing the community and the non-health sectors for primary health care development lie chiefly in communication. Community participation has been well developed in the country for many years.

China is the most notable example of a country where traditional medicine has been well integrated with modern medicine. The community health worker practises both.

The community health workers receive support from structures at different levels which also form a system for mobilizing the community and the health workers. Intersectoral and intrasectoral coordination form part of primary health care.

Community health workers: pillars for health for all: report on an inter-regional conference, Cameroon, 1986. Unpublished WHO document, SHS/CIH/87.2.

Community leaders

The question of the education and training of community leaders in CIH is more difficult, since it is not clear what specific role a community leader would play in CIH and it is impossible to dissociate involvement in health development from involvement in development in general. Community involvement *per se* is the essential process and the health services should try to make health development part of it rather than establish a separate process. Luckily there is now an increasing amount of literature based on the practice of community participation and, as already stated, this should form an important component of community health worker training. For a review of the literature, see Oakley & Marsden (*31*).

If it is accepted, however, that some form of preparation for CIH should be given to community leaders, the following two broad subjects must first be studied:

General health education — It can be argued that a broad campaign of health education in the community is essential for encouraging community involvement in health development. If communities begin to understand health problems better and to single out problems and consider solutions, the basis will have been laid for their involvement in health development (*20*)

Specific areas of knowledge — The organizational and management aspects of community health activities.

— Understanding the development of community-based health programmes and projects.

— Simple methods for communicating ideas on health development.

In preparing community leaders for CIH, a limited and gradual approach is the most appropriate. If progress can be made in the two broad areas mentioned above, at least a basis for CIH will have been laid. It must be acknowledged, however, that at the moment very little thought has been given to the systematic training of community leaders for any kind of formal role in CIH.

Participatory training for "animators"*

People selected as potential "animators" undergo a process of sensitization which helps them to understand better their tasks in releasing people's creative energy and to develop their skills in animation work. This sensitization is a participatory process and has to be sharply distinguished from formal training in which the trainee becomes an object of training and a depository of preconceived knowledge delivered by a trainer. Participatory training programmes cannot in general be pre-structured; they should rather evolve in response to the specific needs and requirements identified by the trainees. An analysis of a number of such participatory training programmes reveals many common features:

(i) A participatory training programme is conducted for small groups, not exceeding about 20 participants, with a relationship of equality between trainee and trainer.

(ii) The starting point is a collective reflection on, and analysis of, the experience that participants have already had in working with rural communities.

(iii) The next step is to analyse the social reality of village situations using the knowledge and experience that participants already have.

(iv) The analysis of the micro-reality is followed by a macro-analysis. Salient features of the national economy, politics and society are brought into the discussion and, where relevant, national and international forces are highlighted.

(v) Next the training programme goes out into the field and participants go to selected villages and live with the communities to study concrete village situations.

(vi) During the field exercise the trainees seek to mobilize the people (or poorer sections) to carry out investigations and analyse their life situations.

*i.e., those who organize and encourage community development activities.

48

> (vii) While continuing their field work, the trainees will regularly to share their experiences and collectively reflect on them. Their learning process thus takes the form of work in the field followed by collective reflection and analysis which enables them to improve the quality of their work and understanding. Experience suggests that it takes between 6 and 12 months for a trainee to acquire the basic skills of participatory development.
>
> Tilakaratna, S. *The animator in participatory rural development.* Geneva, International Labour Office, 1987.

Comment

If it is to have any impact and if it is to lead to a radical shift in health care practice, the education and training of health personnel in the specific knowledge and skills required for CIH must become a basic characteristic of health care training. It is not a question merely of reorienting or restructuring present training curricula in order to incorporate elements of CIH: the very nature of the health care implicit in CIH demands careful reappraisal of the basic approach to health training. CIH implies that health care is not merely a question of providing people with health services or finding technical solutions to health problems. As was seen in Chapter 2, CIH is a partnership and demands a different approach. Merely to slot CIH into existing training practice might weaken its effect.

No textbook on health training for CIH has yet been written although, to judge from experiences in other fields, the task is not now impossible. Before it can be undertaken, however, there are still a number of important matters to be considered:

(i) The balance between the technical and participatory elements in CIH training at different levels needs further research. However, the technical medical content will have to give some ground to the participatory element if CIH is to be practicable.

(ii) Who is going to do the training? Health services probably have facilities for providing the technical medical training, but who is going to provide the participatory element? In this respect health services might have to consider delegating this element of the training to other services, such as the adult education services.

49

(iii) Should the training begin at all levels at the same time? The instinctive answer would probably be 'yes' but in view of the fact that resources are likely to be lacking, it may be necessary initially to concentrate on training community health workers.

It is interesting to speculate, for example, what would happen to training for CIH if the whole participatory element were taken out of the hands of the medical service and made the responsibility of the community development or adult education services.

Methods of promoting CIH

In view of the relative newness of the CIH concept and the fact that in most health services its implementation is still largely at the experimental stage it is not possible for the moment to put forward tried and tested methods of ensuring community involvement in health. Indeed it is doubtful whether it will ever be possible to do so. No methods would be universally applicable. What is referred to here is a range of potential methods that might help develop CIH in a particular context. It is important for health workers to understand the uniqueness of community involvement in any particular context and to choose among these potential methods those best suited to their particular situation. It must be stressed also that successful CIH depends on the selection of appropriate methods just as much as other aspects of development.

The country reports presented at the Brioni meeting underlined the fact that practical experience in community health development has not been extensive or varied enough to enable appropriate methods for CIH to be devised. It was generally recognized that there had so far been little experimentation with CIH methods and that it was time to examine practical experience of participation in other sectoral activities and apply the results to the health sector. Developing CIH methods, however, was considered to present a series of difficulties which would have to be overcome:

(a) The rigid professionalism of formal health services, with the consequent danger that they would not be flexible enough to allow development of CIH skills in their staff. CIH is not a professional activity and cannot flourish within the rigid confines of formal practice.

(b) The fact that in formal health services decisions are taken by professional health staff, so that there is no tradition of allowing communities to become involved in decision-making.

50

(c)   The assumption that formal health staff have a monopoly of health knowledge and that the knowledge possessed by the community is inappropriate, unscientific and not compatible with modern medicine.

(d)   The inflexibility of formal health services and their general unwillingness to contemplate doing things in different ways.

These are formidable obstacles to developing CIH methods and certainly suggest that reorienting health practice based on entrenched professional values and beliefs will not be easy. The first point, therefore, is that to develop methods for ensuring community involvement in health it is essential:

●   to re-examine the training given to health service staff, with particular emphasis on the skills and knowledge needed by staff if they are to be able to promote CIH;

●   to ensure that such training is a two-way undertaking, in which the community and the health service staff establish a basis for future partnership.

If there is no commitment to reorienting professional practice on the part of health service staff, it is highly improbable that suitable methods of promoting CIH can be devised.

It must be assumed, however, that such a commitment will be made so that the basis for methods that will promote CIH can be examined. Methods of promoting community participation in other aspects of development will first be considered.

The basis for methods of promoting CIH

The growing influence of the concept of participation on development practice in general has led to the appearance of a continuously increasing body of literature explaining how participation works and giving details of the methods used. This literature should be consulted by health services promoting CIH. It would be shortsighted for health services to develop methods of promoting CIH without reference to experience in other sectors. Although CIH will undoubtedly have its own particular methodological problems, there is nevertheless a broad strategy of participation that can be applied in all the different sectors of development.

This strategy looks upon participation not as a means of obtaining community support for, or collaboration with, externally designed development projects, but rather as a way of building up an

51

organizational basis for local people to make their opinions known and to be able to negotiate and bargain with the forces that influence their lives. A review of a number of development projects in different parts of the world reveals the following key elements in this strategy of participation (*31*):

(*a*) Participation is a continuing process, for which it is difficult to establish fixed, quantifiable criteria.

(*b*) Communities should be broken down into discrete socioeconomic groups considered as the basic units of developments.

(*c*) Stress is laid on spontaneous initiatives from below, leaving aside all preconceived ideas or standard models.

(*d*) Development should be based on self-reliance; development based on dependence must be eschewed.

(*e*) It is essential that development activities should be controlled by the groups they concern.

(*f*) The groups must learn how to act collectively in their attempts to solve the problems confronting them.

These elements seem to make up a clearly discernible strategy of participation, consistent with CIH. The emphasis is on establishing a basis for authentic participation rather than promoting the acceptance of external development projects. Research has shown that in many instances participatory projects have little substantive existence of their own. Their main purpose is to establish a base for continuing participatory activities, into which, at an appropriate time, the programmes of the different sectors, such as health can be fitted. A CIH strategy, therefore, would have to take into account the development of this base and to accept that CIH cannot occur in isolation but will probably form part of gradually increasing general participatory activities by local people.

There has been little detailed examination of the important elements of a CIH strategy. There are a variety of examples from different countries but they have not yet been consolidated to produce a coherent statement. However three important elements can be deduced from the available material that together could form the basis of a CIH strategy:

● Various forms of mobilization to arouse interest in health development and give it momentum. Mobilization can be centred on particular issues, groups or programmes. It is a first step towards bringing about widespread involvement in health activities (*17*).

● Leadership plays a critical role in developing CIH. It may come from inside or outside the community. Both traditional community leaders and external agents will have a role to play but external agents should never be the dominant force.

● The gradual deprofessionalization of health services and health care will help establish conditions in which CIH can function as a useful partnership between the different categories involved in health development.

One or two writers have taken things a stage further and attempted to set forth in more detail the basis for an alternative strategy of health development which would encourage CIH. A comprehensive statement from Werner (32) described two contrasting approaches to community health development termed community-supportive and community-oppressive. Some of the components that Werner described in contrasting these two approaches are listed below:

Component issue	Community-supportive	Community-oppressive
Initial objectives	Open-ended and flexible	Closed, pre-defined
Method of community participation	Based on time, patience and genuine concern	Participation is bought by financial contribution and giveaways
Sharing of knowledge and skills	From doctor to community health worker to ordinary local resident	Knowledge jealously guarded at each level
Openness and growth of programme	New approaches and improvements encouraged	Rigid standardization
Tacit objective	Social reform	"Don't rock the boat"

The complete list of issues raised by Werner ranges over the whole spectrum of intervention for health development and highlights the very considerable differences and implications of an approach to health development that seeks to rethink and restructure formal health practice and bring it more under the control of local communities. The list is comprehensive and comprises the basic elements in a strategy of health development that would encourage community involvement.

Methods of community participation

A variety of methods can be used to bring about CIH, many of them already common practice in other extension activities but yet to be adopted generally in health development practice. In the past ten years or so imaginative innovations in methods of extension work have aimed at putting new ideas of development into effect and moving away from what was essentially the delivery of knowledge to a variety of methods designed to encourage participation. Such methods have become quite common throughout the world in, for example, rural extension and adult education programmes. However, although they appear to have begun to influence the practice of health care, they cannot yet be said to have had any major impact (*33*).

Although no set of extension methods is universally applicable to all situations, sufficient practical experience has now accumulated to indicate the main elements in those methods. Extension methods to encourage participation consist of a number of clearly definable stages (*31*):

● contact with the target group;

● process of group structuring;

● preparation for work with the group to foster its future participation.

This framework is based on practical experience in a wide range of development projects; it must be emphasized that methods of fostering participation form a continuous process and must strive to establish a sound basis for participation rather than merely organizing community contributions to existing projects. Further examination of the framework reveals a number of common features in the methods, as outlined below.

(*a*) Informal educational methods form the basis for the process. These methods are characterized by:

● their avoidance of directives from above;
● their insistence on discussion and consultation;
● their use of community workers as agents of change;
● their use of concrete project activities as a means of establishing a basis for participation.

These methods are supported by a variety of ways and means of giving concrete and visible effect to the concept of participation:

● group meetings as the basic means of discussing participation;

54

- training sessions and study seminars aimed at enhancing the group's awareness of the advantages of their involvement;
- the use of drama to provoke involvement and discussion;
- the use of simulation or games techniques to analyse the points at issue (*31*).

(*b*) It has already been seen that the development of groups (as opposed to communities) as the basic unit of participation is an important issue in CIH. Increasingly groups are being singled out as the targets of development efforts and the importance of the following aspects of group formation and development is being ever more commonly stressed:

- the way the group came to be formed in the first place, since that will determine the nature and course of its development;
- the definition of group membership and the importance of homogeneity based upon common interest;
- the emergence of a group structure, which will give the group an organizational basis for its participatory activities;
- the size of the group, which will affect the development of the inter-relationships that will form the basis for group solidarity.

Groups are being increasingly used in extension practice, but attitudes vary as to the purpose of their use for participation. Some see the groups essentially as a means of making it easier for group members to enjoy the benefits of development; others see group development as an end in itself and as essential to building up a basis for continued organized participation.

(*c*) Despite the variety of terms used in the literature (promoter, animator, group organizer, facilitator) there is common agreement that some sort of agent is of fundamental importance for participation. In practice, however, there seem to be two quite different interpretations of the agent's primary role:

- to facilitate the access of groups to resources for development (e.g. agriculture, health);
- to support an educational process designed to stimulate awareness within the group and thus begin to develop a basis for more-direct participation in development.

While to some extent the two roles are complementary, they do demand quite different personal characteristics and skills. Ideally there should be a different agent for each role but because of the lack of resources, the two roles are often assumed by the same agent.

55

Methods of community participation

Proshika – Bangladesh

(i) *The methods have 5 main components*:

- determination of marginalized groups;
- the establishment of rapport with those groups;
- training in leadership and organizational skills;
- the formation of village-based groups;
- support of the group development process by the *proshika* "animator".

(ii) *Critical elements in the methods*:

- The animator (*kormy*) is the key element in the whole process. *Proshika* is organized on the basis of a local coordination office, which acts as a base for a team of village *kormys* operating in a given area.

- The provision of credit to help finance agricultural production plans drawn up by the group.

- A management system that delegates responsibility to the local *proshika* offices and actively encourages the taking of decisions jointly by *proshika* and the local groups.

- The encouragement of contacts between groups as a means of building up a broader representative base for the rural poor.

Rahman A., ed. *Grass roots participation and self-reliance*. New Delhi and Oxford, IBH Publishing, 1984, pp. 184–209.

People's Participation Project: FAO

(i) *The methods comprise 3 main elements*:

- The formation and use of local groups to serve as a basis for distributing contributions from outside and undertaking income-generating activities; socioeconomic homogeneity is the critical factor in group membership.

- Local group promoters who advise the groups, support their development and arrange for external support.

- The provision of contributions from outside the groups as the basic lubricant of the participatory process; the contributions support the income-generating activities which are the means by which the groups build up their management and implementation skills.

(ii) *Critical elements in the methods*:

● It is an essential feature of a participatory approach that it should work *with* local people and not *for* them.

● Educational activities must be concerned not with teaching people things but with developing their capacities to analyse, determine and plan a course of action.

● External contributions must be used to give momentum to self-sustaining development.

● A great deal of time must be allowed for any project that seeks to encourage participation.

● The group promoter plays a critical role in the whole process.

Extracted from several reports on the People's Participation Project published by the Food and Agriculture Organization of the United Nations, Rome.

Methods of CIH

A review of the literature suggests that the methodological basis of CIH is still largely underdeveloped. Although there is evidence of the use of some elements of the methods outlined briefly above, in most countries there is little indication that health services have made a systematic effort to use those elements in their practical work. Health service workers still essentially teach their patients; they deal with people on a geographical rather than an economic basis (except, of course, in programmes directed at particular groups, such as maternal and child health) and they are basically concerned with bringing health knowledge and practices to communities rather than developing a basis for community participation. The kinds of method suggested above have thus not been adopted to any significant extent in health service practice. The Brioni meeting confirmed that fact and suggested that it was time for health services to examine the methods used in other sectors, such as agriculture, to promote local involvement, and to apply their findings to the health sector. It was further suggested that the adoption of CIH methods would have strong repercussions on conventional methods of health care, such as the following:

Conventional health care methods	CIH methods
(*a*) Use of individual leaders	Development of group links and interests

(b)	Education as the delivery of knowledge	Education as a joint exploration of knowledge
(c)	Central role of community health worker in individual contact	Community health worker as a group resource
(d)	Individual home visits	Workshops and seminars to discuss health problems and issues
(e)	Individual consultation	Open-door consultation as a mechanism for involvement
(f)	Verbal and written communication of knowledge	Use of games and drama to communicate ideas on health issues

This schematic presentation clearly illustrates the differences between conventional health care methods and the methods used in CIH. While it is not offered as a model, it certainly underlines the fundamental changes in health practice implicit in CIH. While it would probably be generally conceded that the characteristics of conventional health practice are fairly accurately reflected in the first column, it would probably not be universally agreed that the second column represented a generally acceptable CIH methodology. More substantial experimentation on CIH methods will be needed before this can be confirmed.

The past few years, however, have witnessed a number of innovations in health care practice which suggest that health services have begun to be influenced by the CIH concept. Experiments with various educational methods of promoting participation in health (*34*), critical reviews of the basic doctor-patient relationship (*35, 36*) and the preparation of a variety of manuals on health care practice which emphasize participation (*28, 30, 37, 38*) are all examples of the emergence of a different, albeit fragmented, approach to health development. Other innovations that have emerged include:

- self-help groups as the basis for increased community participation in primary health care (*39*);

- village health committees as organizations that can make community participation easier (*40, 41*);

- schoolchildren as health leaders in promoting knowledge of health problems among adults;

- health guardians as providers of health knowledge who thus provide a stronger basis for participation.

All this attests to the increasing influence of CIH and the recognition that community involvement cannot be assumed but has to be developed. Unfortunately, however, the innovations mentioned have still not been very widely practised and knowledge of appropriate methods of CIH still needs to be disseminated on a massive scale.

CIH methods

The Village Health Committee (VHC)
Sequence of actions in setting up a VHC:

(i) Meeting with village or hamlet leaders to explain the purpose of the health project and give a simple description of the plan of operation.

(ii) Gathering information concerning health-related knowledge, attitudes and health practices among villagers.

(iii) Setting up a VHC consisting of selected persons who would help analyse local health needs and plan and execute joint projects for meeting those needs.

(iv) Selecting priority problems and the provision by the village health worker of information on how those problems might be tackled.

(v) Choosing one problem for committee action so as to begin the process of committee involvement.

(vi) Informing the committee of locally feasible solutions to the problems they have singled out.

(vii) Assessing local resources so that the committee will be able to determine what health resources are available locally and what will need to be purchased.

(viii) Setting graduated objectives so that health projects become more amenable to VHC management.

(ix) Assigning responsibilities and establishing a time schedule, including designating the committee members responsible for different activities.

Isely, R. B. & Martin, J. F. The village health committee. *WHO Chronicle*, **31**: 307–315 (1977)

CIH methods

The Health Guardian in Honduras

'Our communities are suspicious, particularly the rural communities. The nurse wears a uniform and is an employee of the government. She is an outsider. We realized then that we were missing the most basic level of health care, the one that was being occupied by the traditional practitioners of medicine: the healers and the midwives. We saw that the community would cooperate with us only if we worked through one of its members.'

And so was born the idea of the *guardianes de salud*. In the eyes of the village people, they are not health officials, but rather community volunteers who collaborate with the Ministry.

In fact, even the traditional practitioners of medicine have in many cases been integrated into the system. As Dr. Fernández explained, these healers (the so-called 'medicine men' or 'witch doctors') are prominent members of many rural communities. They do the best they can with the knowledge and materials available to them. Formerly, they were belittled, even harassed by the official health establishment. Understandably, they felt threatened by the government's programme to extend health services. They stood to lose patients, prestige, and even the fees they charged for their services. They enlisted the aid of their communities and resisted the changes.

The government responded by encouraging the communities to elect these same healers *as guardianes de salud*. Although some still refuse to cooperate and continue to exist side by side with the government programme, many are constructively working in their new role. Said Dr. Fernández: 'We are keeping contact with them to help, and at the same time control, them.'

The integration attempt sometimes backfires. A *guardián de salud* must be literate so that he can read the instructions on medicines and make referrals. But sometimes the community elects an illiterate healer, and the Ministry must reject him. At the same time, I was told about one healer in another part of the country who cannot read or write, but is nevertheless a newspaper correspondent!

Midwives were also drawn into the new system. They too were formerly the objects of scorn. But now the government health workers seek them out, give them a 12-day course and a bag of materials. Every time the midwife visits the local clinics to replenish her supplies, her link with the national health system is reinforced. The *guardián* too is encouraged to collaborate with the midwife by sending her patients. In only a few cases, though, have the midwives themselves become *guardianes de salud*. As Dr. Fernández explained, they are eager to learn new techniques relating to their traditional duties, but are generally too old to take on a wholly new set of responsibilities.

Actually, I found that the concept of community health in Honduras extends considerably beyond the work of these local 'specialists' described above. In addition, the community has a health committee, to which is delegated a large share of the responsibility for planning and carrying out health-related projects. Each committee makes a comprehensive survey of its community and determines its health needs – water, sanitation, etc. Then, in cooperation with representatives of the Ministry of Health, they make up their local plan.

Hamilton, R. Grass roots in health. *Pan American health*, **8** (2): 4–8 (1976)

Comment

Clearly the development of an alternative set of appropriate methods for CIH is only in its initial stages. Health services have become generally entrenched in their professionalism and their adherence to well-proven methods of practice. Hence the very real obstacles to developing CIH methods which were outlined earlier. The issue, of course, is how to break through this entrenched professionalism in health services in order to encourage the emergence of CIH. Finding a solution is clearly not a matter for the health sector alone but will depend on a more general structural change. The evidence suggests that changes are occurring and that health care practice is being influenced by the kinds of method being adopted in other sectors. In order to encourage these changes, a number of steps could be considered:

● linking health practice more directly with practice in other sectors in order to learn from their experience of participation;

● changing the balance in the training of CHWs and other health professionals in order to establish a basis for more direct work in developing CIH;

• producing a manual or guide that relates education for participation directly to the health sector and could be a basic tool for CHWs and other health professionals.

Certainly the last two steps could already be undertaken in regard to training content and format and thus give the necessary impetus to the development of educational methods for the support of CIH.

Evaluation of CIH

As in other forms of development, CIH will have to be evaluated in order to determine the extent and standard of its implementation and its impact on local health care. In practice, however, CIH brings with it a series of as yet unsolved conceptual problems in regard to evaluation. Essentially CIH seeks both to improve the provision of health care in the community and to encourage people's involvement in that health care. It will therefore be necessary to evaluate not only the improvement in health care at the community level but also the nature of the community participation. Similarly in the evaluation of CIH it will be necessary to record and analyse both the quantitative data that can be used to measure the changes that have occurred as a result of CIH and the qualitative aspects of participation.

The practice of CIH, therefore, raises a series of conceptual and methodological problems which have not yet been subjected to systematic examination. There is no shortage of literature on the evaluation of development programmes and projects. Most of it, however, is essentially quantitative in its approach, seeking results that can be quantified and thus serve to measure the changes that have taken place. The same approach could be used for CIH, whose quantitative results it should not be difficult to determine and measure. A WHO study on community participation in water supply and sanitation projects includes a check-list of quantitative indicators (*42*). The more difficult task, both methodologically and in regard to the selection of appropriate indicators, is to evaluate the results of the process of community involvement in health, since processes are essentially qualitative and not normally amenable to quantification for statistical analysis. This difficulty, however, is not confined to CIH (*43*).

In the past few years the burgeoning literature on the evaluation of CIH has made many references to a now widely recognized procedure known as participatory monitoring and evaluation (PME) of development programmes and projects. Reports on health projects in the field increasingly incorporate PME in their discussion of project evaluation. The series of UNICEF/WHO Workshops on Primary Health Care Programmes in the early 1980s worked out certain indicators of participation in such programmes, such as community contribution, organization and attitude change (*44*). A substantial family health programme in Ecuador reported in detail on the PME approach to assessing the benefits of the programme and is particularly revealing in its reports on community opinions on the programme's outcome (*34*). Similarly Rifkin's studies on community participation in health programmes advocate the use of PME in assessing the outcome of those programmes (*45*). In conjunction with the increasing literature on the concept and practice of PME in more general contexts, the studies mentioned have laid the foundations for tackling the still difficult problems encountered in evaluating CIH.

Steps in participatory evaluation

● All those involved in a programme must decide jointly to adopt a participatory approach.

● They must then determine the exact objectives of the evaluation. This is often harder than anticipated.

● When they have reached agreement on the evaluation objectives, they should elect a small group of 'evaluation coordinators' to plan and organize all the details of the evaluation.

● At the same time they must decide what methods will be best for attaining the evaluation objectives. The choice of method, such as analysis of programme records or use of a questionnaire, will also be influenced by the capabilities of the people involved, and by the time and resources available for the evaluation.

● Once these decisions have been taken, an evaluation plan is drawn up in writing, showing why, how, when and where the evaluation will take place, and who will be involved.

● Next the evaluation methods must be set down and tested (for example, a questionnaire may be needed). Selected programme participants will also need training in interviewing, completing written or oral questionnaires, conducting various

---

kinds of checks or examinations, etc. All programme participants should be given explanations of the objectives set and
the general methods to be used in the evaluation. The more
they understand, the more they can participate in the entire
evaluation process, wherever and whenever requested by the
evaluation coordinators.

● Once the evaluaton methods have been prepared and tested, the next step is to use them to collect the facts and
information required for the evaluation.

● The information and data gathered are analysed by the
programme participants. Most of this work will probably be
done by the evaluation coordinators.

● The results of the analysis (or the evaluation findings) are
then reported in written, oral or visual form. There are different
ways of reporting and presenting the evaluation findings to
different groups connected with the programme. For example,
a ministry (or programme funders) will usually need a written
evaluation report, but community participants will be better
able to understand results if they are presented as charts or
pictures, or if they are presented during discussion meetings.

● Programme participants must then decide exactly how the
evaluation results will be used, and how they can help to
improve the performance and effectiveness of the programme.

Feuerstein, M.-T. *Partners in evaluation: evaluating development and community programmes with participants.* London, Macmillan, 1986

Participatory evaluation

Participatory evaluation is a means of achieving the wider
objectives of community participation projects. Community
involvement will enable evaluation to be used as a learning device – a form of functional education which can contribute
to empowerment and partnership. Evaluation needs to be seen
in a changing light: from being commonly a tool for judging
project managers, it can be transformed into a shared process
of community self-assessment and project improvement. It can
be seen not only as a method of pinpointing strengths and
weaknesses in project activities but also as a means of re-
solving them at the same time.

Askew, I. et al. *The community participation approach in family planning
programmes.* London, IPPF, 1986

It is thus necessary to determine the key aspects of CIH to be evaluated and to select appropriate indicators to illustrate the magnitude and nature of the changes that have occurred. This need has not yet been met and, despite the kinds of field experiment mentioned, there is as yet little proven basis for the evaluation of CIH. This state of affairs was confirmed at the Brioni meeting when both regional and country reports contained little of any substance concerning the evaluation of CIH. The participants, however, suggested the following as a tentative basis for an approach to the evaluation of CIH:

Aspect of CIH	Possible indicators
Input	– interpretation of CIH; – availability, type and performance of support mechanisms for CIH; – level of resources available.
Process	– training procedures for CIH; – local administrative procedures for CIH.
Output	– evaluation of procedures and mechanisms to facilitate CIH; – multiplier effect; – institutionalization of the CIH process.
Effect	– increasing involvement of the community in health planning; – level of involvement in, for example, control over resources and choice of technology; – increasing awareness of the causes of poor health; – community initiatives to tackle poor health.
Impact	– increasing accessibility of health services; – gradual establishment of a basis for future community involvement in health care.

This, of course, is simply a list and there is as yet little empirical evidence to support it. The evaluation of CIH is still at the trial-and-error stage and more specific research and investigation will be needed in order to improve the above framework. If, however, it is genuinely wished to evaluate CIH, the following series of steps would seem appropriate:

● Integrate the evaluation of CIH more directly into the broader participatory monitoring and evaluation of other sectors; developments in these sectors could be relevant to the evaluation of CIH.

- Begin the research required to test and define the aspects of CIH that require evaluation and, just as important, select the indicators for this evaluation. Otherwise, the evaluation of CIH will be impossible.

- Use research results to prepare practical field guides to CIH evaluation for health workers.

Ideally, taking the steps outlined above should go hand in hand with increasing practical application of CIH. If evaluation falls behind practice CIH will eventually prove impossible to evaluate. It was with that in mind that the Brioni meeting urged Member countries to give high priority to developing systems for the effective evaluation of CIH.

Research into CIH

There is clearly a need to support the expansion of CIH with appropriate research into those of its aspects that require further clarification. Such research, however, should not be a sectoral activity but should be linked as a matter of principle with research into participation being conducted in other sectors. To date, an impressive amount of research has been done into CIH, although in many instances it has failed to study the details of how CIH works in the field. Similarly much of the emphasis of the research so far has been on integrating CIH into particular aspects of health care, such as tropical disease control; in the health field there has been less research on the concept of CIH itself. A distinct impression is also obtained that many of the publications are not based on empirical research on CIH in the field but tend rather to be exercises in integrating some notion of participation into existing practice. Certainly in the last five years or so health publications have become increasingly influenced by the concept of participation, but the feeling persists that it is a literary exercise. If CIH is not widely practised, it will be difficult to produce material on it that is supported by empirical evidence.

Defining a research schedule for CIH is largely dependent on the resources available and it would therefore be unrealistic to produce a lengthy list of research priorities. It should be noted that substantial research is already being conducted into the processes implicit in CIH and that it would be waste of resources to duplicate that research (47). Moreover, in view of the nature of CIH, research into it should be conducted in a participatory manner. The concept and methods of participatory research have already been incorporated in several instances into research on CIH and that practice should become more widespread (*48*). Finally, the emphasis in research into CIH should be on defining the concept on the basis of practice rather than seeking data and information to confirm a predetermined interpretation. An attempt should be made to derive theory from practice rather than the other way round.

In the short term, attention could be concentrated on the following aspects:

- Adapting the knowledge gained from research into participation in other sectors to the specific requirements of CIH, such as the development of groups or the use of communication materials.

- Determining the implications of CIH for health services at different levels and the kinds of change, both structural and operational, that will be required if CIH is to be successfully promoted.

- Measuring the cost-effectiveness of CIH in relation to its overall objective of increasing basic health service coverage.

These aspects should have priority in CIH research and the research results would certainly help to determine more precisely how CIH can be put into practice. It is unrealistic to expect widespread research into CIH to begin now and duplication must be avoided. A major step forward, however, would be for regional research on these issues to be instituted so that comparative information of direct practical use could be obtained in the not too distant future.

References and notes

1.   Studies dealing with this issue include: UNICEF/WHO: *Community involvement in primary health care: a study of the process of community motivation and continued participation.* Unpublished document, JC21/UNICEF-WHO/77.2.Rev.2; Pan American Health Organization. *Community participation in health and development in the Americas.* Washington, DC, PAHO, 1984 (Scientific Publication No. 473); and Rafkin, S. *Health planning and community participation,* London, Croom Helm, 1985.

2.   Long, N. *Introduction to the sociology of rural development.* London, Tavistock Publications, 1978.

3.   For examples see *Summary of a review of developments in primary health care.* Unpublished WHO document, JC24/UNICEF-WHO/83.2, p. 12.

4. For a discussion of the stages in this process of assessment see Ahmed, M. Community participation: the heart of primary health care. *Contact*, Special series No. 3, 19–21 (1980).

5. *Ideas and action*, No. 145, 1982. This issue is devoted to an examination of primary health care in the context of rural development and raises a number of issues related to the views and opinions of communities on health problems.

6. FAO. *Participation of the poor in rural organizations*. (Rural Organizations Action Programme, 1979).

7. Mensah, E. N. *Mobilization of communities for health development: approaches and constraints* (WHO, undated).

8. Townsley, P. *Mass participation and health care – a case study from the Socialist Republic of Vietnam*. University of Reading, unpublished MA dissertation, 1985. This study is particularly useful for its detailed bibliography.

9. The more common classification of rural communities is one based on differences in communities' abilities to adopt innovations. There is an enormous literature on this subject and the earlier texts are still pertinent. See, for example, Rogers, E. M. *Modernization among peasants*, New York, Holt, Rinehart and Winston, 1971.

10. Pan American Health Organization. *Community participation in health and development in the Americas*. Washington, DC, PAHO, 1984 (Scientific Publication No. 473).

11. See, for example, Galjart, B. *Peasant mobilization and solidarity*. Amsterdam, Van Gorcum, 1976.

12. See, for example, *World health*, June 1980.

13. These principles are drawn from a variety of different texts. For one particularly interesting list of such principles, see Werner, D. Health care and human dignity, *Contact*, Special series, No. 3: 98–100 (1980).

14. Korten, D. & Alfonso, F. *Bureaucracy and the poor*. Manila, Asian Institute of Management, 1981.

15. For a detailed discussion on decentralization in national health services see: *Strengthening ministries of health for primary health care*. Geneva, World Health Organization, 1984 (WHO Offset Publication, No. 82).

16. Hastings, J. E. F. *An analysis of the nine-country study on forms of community participation in primary health care*. WHO Regional Office for Europe, unpublished document, ICP/PHC/301/501.

17. Rifkin, S. *Community involvement in primary health care among the urban poor*. Unpublished WHO document (Available from Division of Strengthening of Health Services, World Health Organization, Geneva, Switzerland.)

18. Two very imaginative and provocative examinations of the issue of local structures and development are provided by Korten, D. Community organization and rural development: a learning process approach, *Public administration review*, September–October 1980, pp. 480–511; and Constantino-

David, K. Issues in community organization, *Community development journal*, 17: 190–201 (1982).

19. For a more detailed discussion of the issues of group development and the emergence of authentic community organizations, see Oakley, P. & Winder, D. The concept and practice of rural social development, *Studies in rural development*, May 1980, pp. 1–84.

20. Fonaroff, A. *Community involvement in health systems for primary health care.* Unpublished WHO document, SHS/83.6.

21. For a wide-ranging discussion and examination of the role of NGOs in development see: Overseas Development Institute. *Proceedings of the Conference on NGOs in Development.* London, ODA, 1987.

22. *Community involvement for health development: report on the Inter-regional Meeting, Brioni, Yugoslavia, 9–14 June, 1985.* Unpublished WHO document, SHS/85.8.

23. See, for example, Tejada Cano, M. From the child to community participation. *Assignment children*, 47/48: 143–164 (1979); Werner, D. & Bower, W. *Helping health workers learn*, Palo Alto, CA, Hesperian Foundation, 1982; Yansheng, M. *Insights from field practice.* UN Inter-Agency Task Force, 1984; Save the Children Fund. *Bridging the gap: a participatory approach to health and nutrition education*, Westport, CT, 1982.

24. *Community health workers: pillars for health for all.* Unpublished WHO document, SHS/CIH 87.2.

25. Flahault, D. & Roemer, M. *Leadership for primary health care.* Geneva, World Health Organization, 1986 (Public Health Papers, No. 82).

26. Flahault, D. The relationship between community health workers, the health services and the community. *WHO Chronicle,* 32: 149–153 (1978).

27. Joint WHO/UNICEF Inter-country Workshop on Primary Health Care. WHO Regional Office for Africa, unpublished document, AFR/CPD/15, 1982.

28. Wood, E. *Community health workers' manual.* Nairobi, African Medical and Research Foundation, 1982.

29. One study, however, does deal with this issue. See Rifkin, S. *Health planning and community participation.* London, Croom Helm, 1985.

30. Save the Children Fund. *Bridging the gap: a participatory approach to health and nutrition education.* Westport, CT, 1982.

31. Oakley, P. & Marsden, P. *Approaches to participation in rural development.* Geneva, International Labour Office, 1985.

32. Werner, D. Health care and human dignity. *Contact*, Special Series, No. 3: 98–100 (1980).

33. There is a need for a soundly based text on how to translate new ideas on development into practice and how to adapt methods accordingly.

34. Overseas Development Administration. *Community participation in family health.* London, ODA, 1980.

35. Kroeger, A. Participatory evaluation of primary health care programmes: an experience with our Indian populations in Ecuador. *Tropical doctor*, 12: 38–43 (1982).

36. Garcia, J. Medicina sin pacientes. *El Tiempo*, 5 February 1986.

37. Werner, D. & Bower, W. *Helping health workers learn*. Palo Alto, CA, Hesperian Foundation, 1982.

38. United States Peace Corps. *Community health education in developing countries*. Washington, 1981.

39. Robinson, D. Self-help groups in primary health care. *World health forum*, 2: 185–191 (1981).

40. Isely, R. B. et al. Community organization as an approach to health education in rural Africa. *International journal of health education*, 22 (3): suppl. (1979).

41. Isely, R. B. & Martin, J. The village health committee. *WHO Chronicle*, 31: 307–315 (1977).

42. Whyte, A. *Guidelines for planning community participation activities in water supply and sanitation projects*. Geneva, World Health Organization, 1986 (WHO Offset Publication, No. 96).

43. For a detailed discussion of the issues involved in this approach to evaluation see: Oakley, P. *The monitoring and evaluation of participation in rural development*. Rome, Food and Agriculture Organization of the United Nations, 1983; also Fernandes, W. & Tandon, R. *Participatory research and evaluation*. New Delhi, Indian Social Institute, 1981.

44. See, for example: WHO/UNICEF. *Report of UNICEF/WHO Intercountry Workshop on Primary Health Care, Dakar, Senegal, 16–20 February 1981*. Unpublished WHO document, PHC/81.1.

45. Rifkin, S. *Health planning and community participation*. London, Croom Helm, 1985.

46. There is a whole range of international, national and nongovernmental bodies currently supporting research into the processes implicit in the concept of community participation, for example, the United Nations Research Institute for Social Development, the International Labour Organisation, the Food and Agriculture Organization of the United Nations, and the Dag Hammarskjold Foundation (Sweden).

47. A possible working definition of participatory research is:

'A method of social investigation involving the full participation of the community; it is an educational process and a means of taking action for development.'

This definition is taken from: Hall, B. *Notes on the development of the concept of participatory research*, Toronto, International Council for Adult Education, 1977. A more recent study is: Rahman, M. A. *The theory and practice of participatory action research*. Geneva, International Labour Office, 1982.

Chapter 4
Future agenda for CIH

CIH is alive and well but making limited progress! That is the inevitable conclusion to be drawn from this study of CIH. The concept does not lack support in the literature or statements of commitment and acceptability. CIH has entered firmly into the vocabulary of health development and is now widely seen as a remedy for the entrenched problems of poor health and inadequate health services. Few, therefore, dispute the importance of CIH or the need for its implementation.

CIH, however, has a much stronger basis on paper than in reality. There have been cases of its successful practice, but they are the exception rather than the rule. Its practice is also highly fragmented and, in many instances, isolated from the formal health services. Where CIH is flourishing, it is inevitably as a result of the energetic efforts of a particular group of health workers; there are few examples as yet in Third World countries of national health services adopting CIH as a general code of practice and reallocating resources accordingly. The result has been that present thinking on CIH is far outstripping its practice. Various sectors of the health system, such as the immunization services or maternal and child health services, have on paper adopted the concept of CIH but without any realistic or detailed assessment of how to put it into practical effect.

CIH certainly constitutes a potentially effective approach to the health problems of the vast majority of the world's peoples. But, as has been demonstrated, its implementation raises many difficult issues. There is a danger that CIH will have only a limited impact and will probably result in collaboration rather than useful participation. This point must really be laboured, since there is a real risk that health services will limit participation to health development and thus fail to take advantage of the experience of other sectors. It must be emphasized that community involvement is the critical process in CIH. Without it CIH becomes merely a means of communicating technical knowledge on health matters.

Before encouraging and developing the practice of CIH, however, the concept itself needs to be more fully understood. So far, in most of the literature on CIH the concept has been defined in narrow collaborative terms. For most writers CIH is a means of extending health service coverage and releasing massive human resources for health development. Such an interpretation of CIH is, however, inadequate and fails to recognize the legitimate demands for worthwhile participation. CIH cannot be regarded as a mere means of technology transfer; it must imply some notion of the transfer of power and authority to local people to enable them to become effectively involved in health development. Thus, although definitions and emphasis may vary in varying situations, the evidence suggests that an effective CIH strategy must comprise the following three elements:

- the development of an organizational basis to facilitate involvement;
- the encouragement of dynamic local self-reliance so that the involvement can be sustained;
- direct control by local people over the resources required for health development.

While it is difficult to make universal statements about CIH, experience of the process of participation in other sectors suggests that those three elements are indispensable to community involvement.

There is now enough literature and practical experience available to justify the conclusion that a solid basis exists for the future development of CIH. There is little point in rekindling old debates or redefining existing issues; the emphasis must now be on creating the conditions for CIH to move forward and be more widely applied. In this respect future action could profitably concentrate on the following aspects:

● Legitimization: a continuous process of making participation an integral part of the existing legal framework. CIH cannot be introduced without regard to the existing political structure but should become an integral part of that structure. Comparative studies of the legal basis of CIH in different political systems would provide invaluable information.

● Changes in formal health services as prerequisites for CIH. Although many studies argue that such changes will be necessary (e.g. in decision-making procedures) little is known to date as to which specific changes would be required, who should make them, and in what order. A more systematic analysis of the probable changes is overdue. Given the nature of CIH these changes will be radical and will inevitably involve a lengthy period of negotiation and implementation.

● Preparation for CIH: determination of the content of CIH training. To date very little formal training for CIH has been undertaken anywhere in the world. The time is now ripe for the development of courses for the different levels in the health services with the emphasis on the balance between technical and non-technical content. It is now time to promote deliberately the training of personnel for CIH.

● Operational guides to support the practice of CIH in the field. At present there are few, if any, guides or manuals on the implementation of CIH. More specific guidance in terms of, for example, group methods of extension, communication processes, and evaluation techniques for CIH would be important supports for the community health worker.

The above issues constitute an agenda for the future development of CIH. The first requires action and negotiation at the national level; for the other three, steps could be taken now to build upon the existing base of CIH. The time has come to move away from simply proclaiming CIH to implementing the kinds of action that will strengthen its practice. It is this application in practice, and not words or promises, that will allow CIH to develop and to exert its influence throughout the world.

WHO publications may be obtained, direct or through booksellers, from:

ALGERIA: Entreprise nationale du Livre (ENAL), 3 bd Zirout Youcef, ALGIERS

ARGENTINA: Carlos Hirsch, SRL, Florida 165, Galerias Güemes, Escritorio 453/465, BUENOS AIRES

AUSTRALIA: Hunter Publications, 58A Gipps Street, COLLINGWOOD, VIC 3066.

AUSTRIA: Gerold & Co., Graben 31, 1011 VIENNA I

BAHRAIN: United Schools International, Arab Region Office, P.O. Box 726, BAHRAIN

BANGLADESH: The WHO Representative, G.P.O. Box 250, DHAKA 5

BELGIUM: *For books:* Office International de Librairie s.a., avenue Marnix 30, 1050 BRUSSELS. *For periodicals and subscriptions:* Office International des Périodiques, avenue Louise 485, 1050 BRUSSELS.

BHUTAN: *see* India, WHO Regional Office

BOTSWANA: Botsalo Books (Pty) Ltd., P.O. Box 1532, GABORONE

BRAZIL: Centro Latinoamericano de Informação em Ciencias de Saúde (BIREME), Organização Panamericana de Saúde, Sector de Publicações, C.P. 20381,- Rua Botucatu 862, 04023 SÃO PAULO, SP

BURMA: *see* India, WHO Regional Office

CAMEROON: Cameroon Book Centre, P.O. Box 123, South West Province, VICTORIA

CANADA: Canadian Public Health Association, 1565 Carling Avenue, Suite 400, OTTAWA, Ont. K1Z 8R1. (Tel: (613) 725-3769. Telex: 21-053-3841)

CHINA: China National Publications Import & Export Corporation, P.O. Box 88, BEIJING (PEKING)

DEMOCRATIC PEOPLE'S REPUBLIC OF KOREA: *see* India, WHO Regional Office

DENMARK: Munksgaard Book and Subscription Service, P.O. Box 2148, 1610 COPENHAGEN K (Tel: + 45 1 12 85 70)

FIJI: The WHO Representative, P.O. Box 113, SUVA

FINLAND: Akateeminen Kirjakauppa, Keskuskatu 2, 00101 HELSINKI 10

FRANCE: Arnette, 2 rue Casimir-Delavigne, 75006 PARIS

GERMAN DEMOCRATIC REPUBLIC: Buchhaus Leipzig, Postfach 140, 701 LEIPZIG

GERMANY FEDERAL REPUBLIC OF: Govi-Verlag GmbH, Ginnheimerstrasse 20, Postfach 5360, 6236 ESCHBORN — Buchhandlung Alexander Horn, Kirchgasse 22, Postfach 3340, 6200 WIESBADEN

GREECE: G.C. Eleftheroudakis S.A., Librairie internationale, rue Nikis 4, 105-63 ATHENS

HONG KONG: Hong Kong Government Information Services, Publication (Sales) Office, Information Services Department, No. 1, Battery Path, Central, HONG KONG.

HUNGARY: Kultura, P.O.B. 149, BUDAPEST 62

ICELAND: Snaebjorn Jonsson & Co., Hafnarstraeti 9, P.O. Box 1131, IS-101 REYKJAVIK

INDIA: WHO Regional Office for South-East Asia, World Health House, Indraprastha Estate, Mahatma Gandhi Road, NEW DELHI 110002

IRAN (ISLAMIC REPUBLIC OF): Iran University Press, 85 Park Avenue, P.O. Box 54/551, TEHRAN

IRELAND: TDC Publishers, 12 North Frederick Street, DUBLIN 1 (Tel: 744835-749677)

ISRAEL: Heiliger & Co., 3 Nathan Strauss Street, JERUSALEM 94227

ITALY: Edizioni Minerva Medica, Corso Bramante 83-85, 10126 TURIN: Via Lamarmora 3, 20100 MILAN: Via Spallanzani 9, 00161 ROME

JAPAN: Maruzen Co. Ltd., P.O. Box 5050, TOKYO International, 100-31

JORDAN: Jordan Book Centre Co. Ltd., University Street, P.O. Box 301 (Al-Jubeiha), AMMAN

KENYA: Text Book Centre Ltd, P.O. Box 47540, NAIROBI

KUWAIT: The Kuwait Bookshops Co. Ltd., Thunayan Al-Ghanem Bldg, P.O. Box 2942, KUWAIT

LAO PEOPLE'S DEMOCRATIC REPUBLIC: The WHO Representative, P.O. Box 343, VIENTIANE

LUXEMBOURG: Librairie du Centre, 49 bd Royal, LUXEMBOURG

A/1/89

WHO publications may be obtained, direct or through booksellers, from:

MALAYSIA: The WHO Representative, Room 1004, 10th Floor, Wisma Lim Foo Yong (formerly Fitzpatrick's Building), Jalan Raja Chulan, KUALA LUMPUR 05–10; P.O. Box 2550, KUALA LUMPUR 01–02; Parry's Book Center, 124–1 Jalan Tun Sambanthan, P.O. Box 10960, 50730 KUALA LUMPUR

MALDIVES: *see* India, WHO Regional Office

MEXICO: Librería Interacademica S.A., Av. Sonora 206, 06100-MÉXICO, D.F.

MONGOLIA: *see* India, WHO Regional Office

MOROCCO: Editions La Porte, 281 avenue Mohammed V, RABAT

NEPAL: *see* India, WHO Regional Office

NETHERLANDS: InOr-Publikaties, P.O. Box 14, 7240 BA LOCHEM

NEW ZEALAND: New Zealand Government Printing Office, Publishing Administration, Private Bag, WELLINGTON; Walter Street, WELLINGTON; World Trade Building, Cubacade, Cuba Street, WELLINGTON. *Government Bookshops at:* Hannaford Burton Building, Rutland Street, Private Bag, AUCKLAND; 159 Hereford Street, Private Bag, CHRISTCHURCH; Alexandra Street, P.O. Box 857, HAMILTON; T & G Building, Princes Street, P.O. Box 1104, DUNEDIN — R. Hill & Son Ltd, Ideal House, Cnr Gillies Avenue & Eden Street, Newmarket, AUCKLAND 1

NORWAY: Tanum — Karl Johan A.S., P.O. Box 1177, Sentrum, N-0107 OSLO 1

PAKISTAN: Mirza Book Agency, 65 Shahrah-E-Quaid-E-Azam, P.O. Box 729, LAHORE 3

PAPUA NEW GUINEA: The WHO Representative, P.O. Box 646, KONEDOBU

PHILIPPINES: World Health Organization, Regional Office for the Western Pacific, P.O. Box 2932, MANILA; National Book Store Inc., 701 Rizal Avenue, P.O. Box 1934, MANILA

PORTUGAL: Livraria Rodrigues, 186 Rua do Ouro, LISBON 2

REPUBLIC OF KOREA: The WHO Representative, Central P.O. Box 540, SEOUL

SAUDI ARABIA: World of Knowledge for Publishing and Distribution, P.O. Box 576, JEDDAH

SINGAPORE: The WHO Representative, 144 Moulmein Road, SINGAPORE 1130; Newton P.O. Box 31, SINGAPORE 9122

SOUTH AFRICA: *Contact major book stores*

SPAIN: Comercial Atheneum S.A., Consejo de Ciento 130–136, 08015 BARCELONA; General Moscardó 29, MADRID 20 — Librería Díaz de Santos, P.O. Box 6050, 28006 MADRID; Balmes 417 y 419, 08022 BARCELONA

SRI LANKA: *see* India, WHO Regional Office

SWEDEN: *For books:* Aktiebolaget C.E. Fritzes Kungl. Hovbokhandel, Regeringsgatan 12, 103 27 STOCKHOLM. *For periodicals:* Wennergren-Williams AB, Box 30004, 104 25 STOCKHOLM

SWITZERLAND: Medizinischer Verlag Hans Huber, Länggassstrasse 76, 3012 BERN 9

THAILAND: *see* India, WHO Regional Office

UNITED KINGDOM: H.M. Stationery Office: 49 High Holborn, LONDON WC1V 6HB; 71 Lothian Road, EDINBURGH EH3 9AZ; 80 Chichester Street, BELFAST BT1 4JY; Brazennose Street, MANCHESTER M60 8AS; 258 Broad Street, BIRMINGHAM B1 2HE; Southey House, Wine Street, BRISTOL BS1 2BQ. *All mail orders should be sent to:* HMSO Publications Centre, 51 Nine Elms Lane, LONDON SW8 5DR

UNITED STATES OF AMERICA: *Copies of individual publications (not subscriptions):* WHO Publications Center USA, 49 Sheridan Avenue, ALBANY, NY 12210. *Subscription orders and correspondence concerning subscriptions should be addressed to the* World Health Organization, Distribution and Sales, 1211 GENEVA 27, Switzerland. *Publications are also available from the* United Nations Bookshop, NEW YORK, NY 10017 (*retail only*)

USSR: *For readers in the USSR requiring Russian editions:* Komsomolskij prospekt 18, Medicinskaja Kniga, MOSCOW — *For readers outside the USSR requiring Russian editions:* Kuzneckij most 18, Meždunarodnaja Kniga, MOSCOW G-200

VENEZUELA: Librería Medica Paris, Apartado 60.681, CARACAS 106

YUGOSLAVIA: Jugoslovenska Knjiga, Terazije 27/II, 11000 BELGRADE

ZIMBABWE: Textbook Sales (PVT) Ltd, 1 Norwich Union Centre, MUTARE

Special terms for developing countries are obtainable on application to the WHO Representatives or WHO Regional Offices listed above or to the World Health Organization, Distribution and Sales Service, 1211 Geneva 27, Switzerland. Orders from countries where sales agents have not yet been appointed may also be sent to the Geneva address, but must be paid for in pounds sterling, US dollars, or Swiss francs. Unesco book coupons may also be used.

Prices are subject to change without notice.